PENGUIN BOOKS — GREAT IDEAS

Hosts of Living Forms

Charles Darwin
1809–82

Charles Darwin

Hosts of Living Forms

PENGUIN BOOKS — GREAT IDEAS

PENGUIN BOOKS

Published by the Penguin Group
Penguin Books Ltd, 80 Strand, London WC2R ORL, England
Penguin Group (USA) Inc., 375 Hudson Street, New York, New York 10014, USA
Penguin Group (Canada), 90 Eglinton Avenue East, Suite 700, Toronto, Ontario, Canada M4P 2Y3
(a division of Pearson Penguin Canada Inc.)
Penguin Ireland, 25 St Stephen's Green, Dublin 2, Ireland (a division of Penguin Books Ltd)
Penguin Group (Australia), 250 Camberwell Road, Camberwell, Victoria 3124,
Australia (a division of Pearson Australia Group Pty Ltd)
Penguin Books India Pvt Ltd, 11 Community Centre,
Panchsheel Park, New Delhi – 110 017, India
Penguin Group (NZ), 67 Apollo Drive, Rosedale, North Shore 0632, New Zealand
(a division of Pearson New Zealand Ltd)
Penguin Books (South Africa) (Pty) Ltd, 24 Sturdee Avenue,
Rosebank, Johannesburg 2196, South Africa

Penguin Books Ltd, Registered Offices: 80 Strand, London WC2R ORL, England

www.penguin.com

First published in *On the Origin of Species* 1859
This selection published in Penguin Books 2010
1

All rights reserved

Set in 11/13 Dante MT Std
Typeset by TexTech International
Printed in England by Clays Ltd, St Ives plc

ISBN: 978-0-141-04810-9

www.greenpenguin.co.uk

Penguin Books is committed to a sustainable future
for our business, our readers and our planet.
The book in your hands is made from paper
certified by the Forest Stewardship Council.

Contents

On the Imperfection of the Geological Record

[Darwin discusses the objection to natural selection presented by the lack of intermediate forms in the fossil record]

The explanation lies, as I believe, in the extreme imperfection of the geological record.

In the first place it should always be borne in mind what sort of intermediate forms must, on my theory, have formerly existed. I have found it difficult, when looking at any two species, to avoid picturing to myself, forms *directly* intermediate between them. But this is a wholly false view; we should always look for forms intermediate between each species and a common but unknown progenitor; and the progenitor will generally have differed in some respects from all its modified descendants. To give a simple illustration: the fantail and pouter pigeons have both descended from the rock-pigeon; if we possessed all the intermediate varieties which have ever existed, we should have an extremely close series between both and the rock-pigeon; but we should have no varieties directly intermediate between the fantail and pouter; none, for instance, combining a tail somewhat expanded with a crop somewhat enlarged, the characteristic features of these two breeds. These two breeds, moreover, have become so much modified, that if we had no historical or indirect evidence regarding their origin, it would not have been possible to have determined from a mere comparison of their structure with that of the rock-pigeon, whether they had descended from this species or from some other allied species, such as C. oenas.

So with natural species, if we look to forms very distinct, for instance to the horse and tapir, we have no reason to suppose that links ever existed directly intermediate between them, but between each and an unknown common parent. The common parent will have had in its whole organisation much general resemblance to the tapir and to the horse; but in some points of structure may have differed considerably from both, even perhaps more than they differ from each other. Hence in all such cases, we should be unable to recognise the parent-form of any two or more species, even if we closely compared the structure of the parent with that of its modified descendants, unless at the same time we had a nearly perfect chain of the intermediate links.

It is just possible by my theory, that one of two living forms might have descended from the other; for instance, a horse from a tapir; and in this case *direct* intermediate links will have existed between them. But such a case would imply that one form had remained for a very long period unaltered, whilst its descendants had undergone a vast amount of change; and the principle of competition between organism and organism, between child and parent, will render this a very rare event; for in all cases the new and improved forms of life will tend to supplant the old and unimproved forms.

By the theory of natural selection all living species have been connected with the parent-species of each genus, by differences not greater than we see between the varieties of the same species at the present day; and these parent-species, now generally extinct, have in their turn been similarly connected with more ancient species; and so on backwards, always converging to the common ancestor of each great class. So that the number of intermediate and transitional links, between all living and extinct species, must have been inconceivably great. But assuredly, if this theory be true, such have lived upon this earth.

On the lapse of Time – Independently of our not finding fossil remains of such infinitely numerous connecting links, it may be objected, that time will not have sufficed for so great an amount of organic change, all changes having been effected very slowly through natural selection. It is hardly possible for me even to recall to the reader, who may not be a practical geologist, the facts leading the mind feebly to comprehend the lapse of time. He who can read Sir Charles Lyell's grand work on the Principles of Geology, which the future historian will recognise as having produced a revolution in natural science, yet does not admit how incomprehensibly vast have been the past periods of time, may at once close this volume. Not that it suffices to study the Principles of Geology, or to read special treatises by different observers on separate formations, and to mark how each author attempts to give an inadequate idea of the duration of each formation or even each stratum. A man must for years examine for himself great piles of superimposed strata, and watch the sea at work grinding down old rocks and making fresh sediment, before he can hope to comprehend anything of the lapse of time, the monuments of which we see around us.

It is good to wander along lines of sea-coast, when formed of moderately hard rocks, and mark the process of degradation. The tides in most cases reach the cliffs only for a short time twice a day, and the waves eat into them only when they are charged with sand or pebbles; for there is reason to believe that pure water can effect little or nothing in wearing away rock. At last the base of the cliff is undermined, huge fragments fall down, and these remaining fixed, have to be worn away, atom by atom, until reduced in size they can be rolled about by the waves, and then are more quickly ground into pebbles, sand, or mud. But how often do we see along the bases of retreating cliffs rounded boulders, all thickly clothed by marine productions, showing how little they are abraded and how seldom they are rolled about! Moreover, if we follow for a few miles any line of rocky cliff, which is undergoing degradation, we find that it is only here and there, along a short length or round a promontory, that the cliffs are at the present time suffering. The appearance of the surface and the vegetation show that elsewhere years have elapsed since the waters washed their base.

He who most closely studies the action of the sea on our shores, will, I believe, be most deeply impressed with the slowness with which rocky coasts are worn away. The observations on this head by Hugh Miller, and by that excellent observer Mr Smith of Jordan Hill, are most impressive. With the mind thus impressed, let any one examine beds of conglomerate many thousand feet in thickness, which, though probably formed at a quicker rate than many other deposits, yet, from being formed of worn and rounded pebbles, each of which bears the stamp of time, are good to show how slowly the mass has been accumulated. Let him remember Lyell's profound remark, that the thickness and extent of sedimentary formations are the result and measure of the degradation which the earth's crust has elsewhere suffered. And what an amount of degradation is implied by the sedimentary deposits of many countries! Professor Ramsay has given me the maximum thickness, in most cases from actual measurement, in a few cases from estimate, of each formation in different parts of Great Britain; and this is the result: –

	Feet
Palaeozoic strata (not including igneous beds)	57,154
Secondary strata	13,190
Tertiary strata	2,240

– making altogether 72,584 feet; that is, very nearly thirteen and three-quarters British miles. Some of these formations, which are represented in England by thin beds, are thousands of feet in thickness on the Continent. Moreover, between each successive formation, we have, in the opinion of most geologists, enormously long blank periods. So that the lofty pile of sedimentary rocks in Britain, gives but an inadequate idea of the time which has elapsed during their accumulation; yet what time this must have consumed! Good observers have estimated that sediment is deposited by the great Mississippi river at the rate of only 600 feet in a hundred thousand years.

This estimate may be quite erroneous; yet, considering over what wide spaces very fine sediment is transported by the currents of the sea, the process of accumulation in any one area must be extremely slow.

But the amount of denudation which the strata have in many places suffered, independently of the rate of accumulation of the degraded matter, probably offers the best evidence of the lapse of time. I remember having been much struck with the evidence of denudation, when viewing volcanic islands, which have been worn by the waves and pared all round into perpendicular cliffs of one or two thousand feet in height; for the gentle slope of the lava-streams, due to their formerly liquid state, showed at a glance how far the hard, rocky beds had once extended into the open ocean. The same story is still more plainly told by faults – those great cracks along which the strata have been upheaved on one side, or thrown down on the other, to the height or depth of thousands of feet; for since the crust cracked, the surface of the land has been so completely planed down by the action of the sea, that no trace of these vast dislocations is externally visible.

The Craven fault, for instance, extends for upwards of 30 miles, and along this line the vertical displacement of the strata has varied from 600 to 3000 feet. Prof. Ramsay has published an account of a downthrow in Anglesea of 2300 feet; and he informs me that he fully believes there is one in Merionethshire of 12,000 feet; yet in these cases there is nothing on the surface to show such prodigious movements; the pile of rocks on the one or other side having been smoothly swept away. The consideration of these facts impresses my mind almost in the same manner as does the vain endeavour to grapple with the idea of eternity.

I am tempted to give one other case, the well-known one of the denudation of the Weald. Though it must be admitted that the denudation of the Weald has been a mere trifle, in comparison with that which has removed masses of our palaeozoic strata, in parts ten thousand feet in thickness, as shown in Prof. Ramsay's masterly memoir on this subject. Yet it is an admirable lesson to stand on the North Downs and to look at the distant South Downs; for, remembering that at no great distance to the west the northern and southern escarpments meet and close, one can safely picture to oneself the great dome of rocks which must have covered up the Weald within so limited a period as since the latter part of the Chalk formation. The distance from the northern to the southern Downs is about 22 miles, and the thickness of the several formations is on an average about 1100 feet, as I am informed by Prof. Ramsay. But if, as some geologists suppose, a range of older rocks underlies the Weald, on the flanks of which the overlying sedimentary deposits might have accumulated in thinner masses than elsewhere, the above estimate would be erroneous; but this source of doubt probably would not greatly affect the estimate as applied to the western extremity of the district. If, then, we knew the rate at which the sea commonly wears away a line of cliff of any given height, we could measure the time requisite to have denuded the Weald. This, of course, cannot be done; but we may, in order to form some crude notion on the subject, assume that the sea would eat into cliffs 500 feet in height at the rate of one inch in a century. This will at first appear much too small an allowance; but it is the same as if we were to assume a cliff one yard in height to be eaten back along a whole line of coast at the rate of one yard in nearly every twenty-two years. I doubt whether any rock, even as soft as chalk, would yield at this rate excepting on the most exposed coasts; though no doubt the degradation of a lofty cliff would be more rapid from the breakage of the fallen fragments. On the other hand, I do not believe that any line of coast, ten or twenty miles in length, ever suffers degradation at the same time along its whole indented length; and we must remember that almost all strata contain harder layers or nodules, which from long resisting attrition form a break-water at the base. Hence, under ordinary circumstances, I conclude that for a cliff 500 feet in height, a denudation of one inch per century for the whole length would be an ample allowance. At this rate, on the above data, the denudation of the Weald must have required 306,662,400 years; or say three hundred million years.

The action of fresh water on the gently inclined Weal-den district, when upraised, could hardly have been great, but it would somewhat reduce the above estimate. On the other hand, during oscillations of level, which we know this area has undergone, the surface may have existed for millions of years as land, and thus have escaped the action of the sea: when deeply submerged for perhaps equally long periods, it would, likewise, have escaped the action of the coast-waves. So that in all probability a far longer period than 300 million years has elapsed since the latter part of the Secondary period.

I have made these few remarks because it is highly important for us to gain some notion, however imperfect, of the lapse of years. During each of these years, over the whole world, the land and the water has been peopled by hosts of living forms. What an infinite number of generations, which the mind cannot grasp, must have succeeded each other in the long roll of years! Now turn to our richest geological museums, and what a paltry display we behold!

On the poorness of our Palaeontological collections – That our palaeontological collections are very imperfect, is admitted by every one. The remark of that admirable palaeontologist, the late Edward Forbes, should not be forgotten, namely, that numbers of our fossil species are known and named from single and often broken specimens, or from a few specimens collected on some one spot. Only a small portion of the surface of the earth has been geologically explored, and no part with sufficient care, as the important discoveries made every year in Europe prove. No organism wholly soft can be preserved. Shells and bones will decay and disappear when left on the bottom of the sea, where sediment is not accumulating. I believe we are continually taking a most erroneous view, when we tacitly admit to ourselves that sediment is being deposited over nearly the whole bed of the sea, at a rate sufficiently quick to embed and preserve fossil remains. Throughout an enormously large proportion of the ocean, the bright blue tint of the water bespeaks its purity. The many cases on record of a formation conformably covered, after an enormous interval of time, by another and later formation, without the underlying bed having suffered in the interval any wear and tear, seem explicable only on the view of the bottom of the sea not rarely lying for ages in an unaltered condition. The remains which do become embedded, if in sand or gravel, will when the beds are upraised generally be dissolved by the percolation of rain-water. I suspect that but few of the very many animals which live on the beach between high and low watermark are preserved. For instance, the several species of the Chthamalinae (a subfamily of sessile cirripedes) coat the rocks all over the world in infinite numbers: they are all strictly littoral, with the exception of a single Mediterranean species, which inhabits deep water and has been found fossil in Sicily, whereas not one other species has hitherto been found in any tertiary formation: yet it is now known that the genus Chthamalus existed during the Chalk period. The molluscan genus Chiton offers a partially analogous case.

With respect to the terrestrial productions which lived during the Secondary and Palaeozoic periods, it is superfluous to state that our evidence from fossil remains is fragmentary in an extreme degree. For instance, not a land shell is known belonging to either of these vast periods, with one exception discovered by Sir C. Lyell in the carboniferous strata of North America. In regard to mammiferous remains, a single glance at the historical table published in the Supplement to Lyell's Manual, will bring home the truth, how accidental and rare is their preservation, far better than pages of detail. Nor is their rarity surprising, when we remember how large a proportion of the bones of tertiary mammals have been discovered either in caves or in lacustrine deposits; and that not a cave or true lacustrine bed is known belonging to the age of our secondary or palaeozoic formations.

But the imperfection in the geological record mainly results from another and more important cause than any of the foregoing; namely, from the several formations being separated from each other by wide intervals of time. When we see the formations tabulated in written works, or when we follow them in nature, it is difficult to avoid believing that they are closely consecutive. But we know, for instance, from Sir R. Murchison's great work on Russia, what wide gaps there are in that country between the superimposed formations; so it is in North America, and in many other parts of the world. The most skilful geologist, if his attention had been exclusively confined to these large territories, would never have suspected that during the periods which were blank and barren in his own country, great piles of sediment, charged with new and peculiar forms of life, had elsewhere been accumulated. And if in each separate territory, hardly any idea can be formed of the length of time which has elapsed between the consecutive formations, we may infer that this could nowhere be ascertained. The frequent and great changes in the mineralogical composition of consecutive formations, generally implying great changes in the geography of the surrounding lands, whence the sediment has been derived, accords with the belief of vast intervals of time having elapsed between each formation.

But we can, I think, see why the geological formations of each region are almost invariably intermittent; that is, have not followed each other in close sequence. Scarcely any fact struck me more when examining many hundred miles of the South American coasts, which have been upraised several hundred feet within the recent period, than the absence of any recent deposits sufficiently extensive to last for even a short geological period. Along the whole west coast, which is inhabited by a peculiar marine fauna, tertiary beds are so scantily developed, that no record of several successive and peculiar marine faunas will probably be preserved to a distant age. A little reflection will explain why along the rising coast of the western side of South America, no extensive formations with recent or tertiary remains can anywhere be found, though the supply of sediment must for ages have been great, from the enormous degradation of the coast-rocks and from muddy streams entering the sea. The explanation, no doubt, is, that the littoral and sub-littoral deposits are continually worn away, as soon as they are brought up by the slow and gradual rising of the land within the grinding action of the coast-waves.

We may, I think, safely conclude that sediment must be accumulated in extremely thick, solid, or extensive masses, in order to withstand the incessant action of the waves, when first upraised and during subsequent oscillations of level. Such thick and extensive accumulations of sediment may be formed in two ways; either, in profound depths of the sea, in which case, judging from the researches of E. Forbes, we may conclude that the bottom will be inhabited by extremely few animals, and the mass when upraised will give a most imperfect record of the forms of life which then existed; or, sediment may be accumulated to any thickness and extent over a shallow bottom, if it continue slowly to subside. In this latter case, as long as the rate of subsidence and supply of sediment nearly balance each other, the sea will remain shallow and favourable for life, and thus a fossiliferous formation thick enough, when upraised, to resist any amount of degradation, may be formed.

I am convinced that all our ancient formations, which are rich in fossils, have thus been formed during subsidence. Since publishing my views on this subject in 1845, I have watched the progress of Geology, and have been surprised to note how author after author, in treating of this or that great formation, has come to the conclusion that it was accumulated during subsidence. I may add, that the only ancient tertiary formation on the west coast of South America, which has been bulky enough to resist such degradation as it has as yet suffered, but which will hardly last to a distant geological age, was certainly deposited during a downward oscillation of level, and thus gained considerable thickness.

All geological facts tell us plainly that each area has undergone numerous slow oscillations of level, and apparently these oscillations have affected wide spaces. Consequently formations rich in fossils and sufficiently thick and extensive to resist subsequent degradation, may have been formed over wide spaces during periods of subsidence, but only where the supply of sediment was sufficient to keep the sea shallow and to embed and preserve the remains before they had time to decay. On the other hand, as long as the bed of the sea remained stationary, *thick* deposits could not have been accumulated in the shallow parts, which are the most favourable to life. Still less could this have happened during the alternate periods of elevation; or, to speak more accurately, the beds which were then accumulated will have been destroyed by being upraised and brought within the limits of the coast-action.

Thus the geological record will almost necessarily be rendered intermittent. I feel much confidence in the truth of these views, for they are in strict accordance with the general principles inculcated by Sir C. Lyell; and E. Forbes independently arrived at a similar conclusion.

One remark is here worth a passing notice. During periods of elevation the area of the land and of the adjoining shoal parts of the sea will be increased, and new stations will often be formed; – all circumstances most favourable, as previously explained, for the formation of new varieties and species; but during such periods there will generally be a blank in the geological record. On the other hand, during subsidence, the inhabited area and number of inhabitants will decrease (excepting the productions on the shores of a continent when first broken up into an archipelago), and consequently during subsidence, though there will be much extinction, fewer new varieties or species will be formed; and it is during these very periods of subsidence, that our great deposits rich in fossils have been accumulated. Nature may almost be said to have guarded against the frequent discovery of her transitional or linking forms.

From the foregoing considerations it cannot be doubted that the geological record, viewed as a whole, is extremely imperfect; but if we confine our attention to any one formation, it becomes more difficult to understand, why we do not therein find closely graduated varieties between the allied-species which lived at its commencement and at its close. Some cases are on record of the same species presenting distinct varieties in the upper and lower parts of the same formation, but, as they are rare, they may be here passed over. Although each formation has indisputably required a vast number of years for its deposition, I can see several reasons why each should not include a graduated series of links between the species which then lived; but I can by no means pretend to assign due proportional weight to the following considerations.

Although each formation may mark a very long lapse of years, each perhaps is short compared with the period requisite to change one species into another. I am aware that two palaeontologists, whose opinions are worthy of much deference, namely Bronn and Woodward, have concluded that the average duration of each formation is twice or thrice as long as the average duration of specific forms. But insuperable difficulties, as it seems to me, prevent us coming to any just conclusion on this head. When we see a species first appearing in the middle of any formation, it would be rash in the extreme to infer that it had not elsewhere previously existed. So again when we find a species disappearing before the uppermost layers have been deposited, it would be equally rash to suppose that it then became wholly extinct. We forget how small the area of Europe is compared with the rest of the world; nor have the several stages of the same formation throughout Europe been correlated with perfect accuracy.

With marine animals of all kinds, we may safely infer a large amount of migration during climatal and other changes; and when we see a species first appearing in any formation, the probability is that it only then first immigrated into that area. It is well known, for instance, that several species appeared somewhat earlier in the palaeozoic beds of North America than in those of Europe; time having apparently been required for their migration from the American to the European seas. In examining the latest deposits of various quarters of the world, it has everywhere been noted, that some few still existing species are common in the deposit, but have become extinct in the immediately surrounding sea; or, conversely, that some are now abundant in the neighbouring sea, but are rare or absent in this particular deposit. It is an excellent lesson to reflect on the ascertained amount of migration of the inhabitants of Europe during the Glacial period, which forms only a part of one whole geological period; and likewise to reflect on the great changes of level, on the inordinately great change of climate, on the prodigious lapse of time, all included within this same Glacial period. Yet it may be doubted whether in any quarter of the world, sedimentary deposits, *including fossil remains*, have gone on accumulating within the same area during the whole of this period. It is not, for instance, probable that sediment was deposited during the whole of the glacial period near the mouth of the Mississippi, within that limit of depth at which marine animals can flourish; for we know what vast geographical changes occurred in other parts of America during this space of time. When such beds as were deposited in shallow water near the mouth of the Mississippi during some part of the Glacial period shall have been upraised, organic remains will probably first appear and disappear at different levels, owing to the migration of species and to geographical changes. And in the distant future, a geologist examining these beds, might be tempted to conclude that the average duration of life of the embedded fossils had been less than that of the glacial period, instead of having been really far greater, that is extending from before the glacial epoch to the present day.

In order to get a perfect gradation between two forms in the upper and lower parts of the same formation, the deposit must have gone on accumulating for a very long period, in order to have given sufficient time for the slow process of variation; hence the deposit will generally have to be a very thick one; and the species undergoing modification will have had to live on the same area throughout this whole time. But we have seen that a thick fossiliferous formation can only be accumulated during a period of subsidence; and to keep the depth approximately the same, which is necessary in order to enable the same species to live on the same space, the supply of sediment must nearly have counterbalanced the amount of subsidence. But this same movement of subsidence will often tend to sink the area whence the sediment is derived, and thus diminish the supply whilst the downward movement continues. In fact, this nearly exact balancing between the supply of sediment and the amount of subsidence is probably a rare contingency; for it has been observed by more than one palaeontologist, that very thick deposits are usually barren of organic remains, except near their upper or lower limits.

It would seem that each separate formation, like the whole pile of formations in any country, has generally been intermittent in its accumulation. When we see, as is so often the case, a formation composed of beds of different mineralogical composition, we may reasonably suspect that the process of deposition has been much interrupted, as a change in the currents of the sea and a supply of sediment of a different nature will generally have been due to geographical changes requiring much time. Nor will the closest inspection of a formation give any idea of the time which its deposition has consumed. Many instances could be given of beds only a few feet in thickness, representing formations, elsewhere thousands of feet in thickness, and which must have required an enormous period for their accumulation; yet no one ignorant of this fact would have suspected the vast lapse of time represented by the thinner formation. Many cases could be given of the lower beds of a formation having been upraised, denuded, submerged, and then re-covered by the upper beds of the same formation – facts, showing what wide, yet easily overlooked, intervals have occurred in its accumulation. In other cases we have the plainest evidence in great fossilised trees, still standing upright as they grew, of many long intervals of time and changes of level during the process of deposition, which would never even have been suspected, had not the trees chanced to have been preserved: thus, Messrs. Lyell and Dawson found carboniferous beds 1400 feet thick in Nova Scotia, with ancient root-bearing strata, one above the other, at no less than sixty-eight different levels. Hence, when the same species occur at the bottom, middle, and top of a formation, the probability is that they have not lived on the same spot during the whole period of deposition, but have disappeared and reappeared, perhaps many times, during the same geological period. So that if such species were to undergo a considerable amount of modification during any one geological period, a section would not probably include all the fine intermediate gradations which must on my theory have existed between them, but abrupt, though perhaps very slight, changes of form.

It is all-important to remember that naturalists have no golden rule by which to distinguish species and varieties; they grant some little variability to each species, but when they meet with a somewhat greater amount of difference between any two forms, they rank both as species, unless they are enabled to connect them together by close intermediate gradations. And this from the reasons just assigned we can seldom hope to effect in any one geological section. Supposing B and C to be two species, and a third, A, to be found in an underlying bed; even if A were strictly intermediate between B and C, it would simply be ranked as a third and distinct species, unless at the same time it could be most closely connected with either one or both forms by intermediate varieties. Nor should it be forgotten, as before explained, that A might be the actual progenitor of B and C, and yet might not at all necessarily be strictly intermediate between them in all points of structure. So that we might obtain the parent-species and its several modified descendants from the lower and upper beds of a formation, and unless we obtained numerous transitional gradations, we should not recognise their relationship, and should consequently be compelled to rank them all as distinct species.

It is notorious on what excessively slight differences many palaeontologists have founded their species; and they do this the more readily if the specimens come from different sub-stages of the same formation. Some experienced conchologists are now sinking many of the very fine species of D'Orbigny and others into the rank of varieties; and on this view we do find the kind of evidence of change which on my theory we ought to find. Moreover, if we look to rather wider intervals, namely, to distinct but consecutive stages of the same great formation, we find that the embedded fossils, though almost universally ranked as specifically different, yet are far more closely allied to each other than are the species found in more widely separated formations; but to this subject I shall have to return in the following chapter.

One other consideration is worth notice: with animals and plants that can propagate rapidly and are not highly locomotive, there is reason to suspect, as we have formerly seen, that their varieties are generally at first local; and that such local varieties do not spread widely and supplant their parent-forms until they have been modified and perfected in some considerable degree. According to this view, the chance of discovering in a formation in any one country all the early stages of transition between any two forms, is small, for the successive changes are supposed to have been local or confined to some one spot. Most marine animals have a wide range; and we have seen that with plants it is those which have the widest range, that oftenest present varieties; so that with shells and other marine animals, it is probably those which have had the widest range, far exceeding the limits of the known geological formations of Europe, which have oftenest given rise, first to local varieties and ultimately to new species; and this again would greatly lessen the chance of our being able to trace the stages of transition in any one geological formation.

It should not be forgotten, that at the present day, with perfect specimens for examination, two forms can seldom be connected by intermediate varieties and thus proved to be the same species, until many specimens have been collected from many places; and in the case of fossil species this could rarely be effected by palaeontologists. We shall, perhaps, best perceive the improbability of our being enabled to connect species by numerous, fine, intermediate, fossil links, by asking ourselves whether, for instance, geologists at some future period will be able to prove, that our different breeds of cattle, sheep, horses, and dogs have descended from a single stock or from several aboriginal stocks; or, again, whether certain seashells inhabiting the shores of North America, which are ranked by some conchologists as distinct species from their European representatives, and by other conchologists as only varieties, are really varieties or are, as it is called, specifically distinct. This could be effected only by the future geologist discovering in a fossil state numerous intermediate gradations; and such success seems to me improbable in the highest degree.

Geological research, though it has added numerous species to existing and extinct genera, and has made the intervals between some few groups less wide than they otherwise would have been, yet has done scarcely anything in breaking down the distinction between species, by connecting them together by numerous, fine, intermediate varieties; and this not having been effected, is probably the gravest and most obvious of all the many objections which may be urged against my views. Hence it will be worth while to sum up the foregoing remarks, under an imaginary illustration. The Malay Archipelago is of about the size of Europe from the North Cape to the Mediterranean, and from Britain to Russia; and therefore equals all the geological formations which have been examined with any accuracy, excepting those of the United States of America. I fully agree with Mr Godwin-Austen, that the present condition of the Malay Archipelago, with its numerous large islands separated by wide and shallow seas, probably represents the former state of Europe, when most of our formations were accumulating. The Malay Archipelago is one of the richest regions of the whole world in organic beings; yet if all the species were to be collected which have ever lived there, how imperfectly would they represent the natural history of the world!

But we have every reason to believe that the terrestrial productions of the archipelago would be preserved in an excessively imperfect manner in the formations which we suppose to be there accumulating. I suspect that not many of the strictly littoral animals, or of those which lived on naked submarine rocks, would be embedded; and those embedded in gravel or sand, would not endure to a distant epoch. Wherever sediment did not accumulate on the bed of the sea, or where it did not accumulate at a sufficient rate to protect organic bodies from decay, no remains could be preserved.

In our archipelago, I believe that fossiliferous formations could be formed of sufficient thickness to last to an age, as distant in futurity as the secondary formations lie in the past, only during periods of subsidence. These periods of subsidence would be separated from each other by enormous intervals, during which the area would be either stationary or rising; whilst rising, each fossiliferous formation would be destroyed, almost as soon as accumulated, by the incessant coast-action, as we now see on the shores of South America. During the periods of subsidence there would probably be much extinction of life; during the periods of elevation, there would be much variation, but the geological record would then be least perfect.

It may be doubted whether the duration of any one great period of subsidence over the whole or part of the archipelago, together with a contemporaneous accumulation of sediment, would *exceed* the average duration of the same specific forms; and these contingencies are indispensable for the preservation of all the transitional gradations between any two or more species. If such gradations were not fully preserved, transitional varieties would merely appear as so many distinct species. It is, also, probable that each great period of subsidence would be interrupted by oscillations of level, and that slight climatal changes would intervene during such lengthy periods; and in these cases the inhabitants of the archipelago would have to migrate, and no closely consecutive record of their modifications could be preserved in any one formation.

Very many of the marine inhabitants of the archipelago now range thousands of miles beyond its confines; and analogy leads me to believe that it would be chiefly these far-ranging species which would oftenest produce new varieties; and the varieties would at first generally be local or confined to one place, but if possessed of any decided advantage, or when further modified and improved, they would slowly spread and supplant their parent-forms. When such varieties returned to their ancient homes, as they would differ from their former state, in a nearly uniform, though perhaps extremely slight degree, they would, according to the principles followed by many palaeontologists, be ranked as new and distinct species.

If then, there be some degree of truth in these remarks, we have no right to expect to find in our geological formations, an infinite number of those fine transitional forms, which on my theory assuredly have connected all the past and present species of the same group into one long and branching chain of life. We ought only to look for a few links, some more closely, some more distantly related to each other; and these links, let them be ever so close, if found in different stages of the same formation, would, by most palaeontologists, be ranked as distinct species. But I do not pretend that I should ever have suspected how poor a record of the mutations of life, the best preserved geological section presented, had not the difficulty of our not discovering innumerable transitional links between the species which appeared at the commencement and close of each formation, pressed so hardly on my theory.

On the sudden appearance of whole groups of Allied Species – The abrupt manner in which whole groups of species suddenly appear in certain formations, has been urged by several palaeontologists, for instance, by Agassiz, Pictet, and by none more forcibly than by Professor Sedgwick, as a fatal objection to the belief in the transmutation of species. If numerous species, belonging to the same genera or families, have really started into life all at once, the fact would be fatal to the theory of descent with slow modification through natural selection. For the development of a group of forms, all of which have descended from some one progenitor, must have been an extremely slow process; and the progenitors must have lived long ages before their modified descendants. But we continually over-rate the perfection of the geological record, and falsely infer, because certain genera or families have not been found beneath a certain stage, that they did not exist before that stage. We continually forget how large the world is, compared with the area over which our geological formations have been carefully examined; we forget that groups of species may elsewhere have long existed and have slowly multiplied before they invaded the ancient archipelagoes of Europe and of the United States. We do not make due allowance for the enormous intervals of time, which have probably elapsed between our consecutive formations – longer perhaps in some cases than the time required for the accumulation of each formation. These intervals will have given time for the multiplication of species from some one or some few parent-forms; and in the succeeding formation such species will appear as if suddenly created.

I may here recall a remark formerly made, namely that it might require a long succession of ages to adapt an organism to some new and peculiar line of life, for instance to fly through the air; but that when this had been effected, and a few species had thus acquired a great advantage over other organisms, a comparatively short time would be necessary to produce many divergent forms, which would be able to spread rapidly and widely throughout the world.

I will now give a few examples to illustrate these remarks; and to show how liable we are to error in supposing that whole groups of species have suddenly been produced. I may recall the well-known fact that in geological treatises, published not many years ago, the great class of mammals was always spoken of as having abruptly come in at the commencement of the tertiary series. And now one of the richest known accumulations of fossil mammals belongs to the middle of the secondary series; and one true mammal has been discovered in the new red sandstone at nearly the commencement of this great series. Cuvier used to urge that no monkey occurred in any tertiary stratum; but now extinct species have been discovered in India, South America, and in Europe even as far back as the eocene stage. The most striking case, however, is that of the Whale family; as these animals have huge bones, are marine, and range over the world, the fact of not a single bone of a whale having been discovered in any secondary formation, seemed fully to justify the belief that this great and distinct order had been suddenly produced in the interval between the latest secondary and earliest tertiary formation. But now we may read in the Supplement to Lyell's 'Manual', published in 1858, clear evidence of the existence of whales in the upper greensand, some time before the close of the secondary period.

I may give another instance, which from having passed under my own eyes has much struck me. In a memoir on

Fossil Sessile Cirripedes, I have stated that, from the number of existing and extinct tertiary species; from the extraordinary abundance of the individuals of many species all over the world, from the Arctic regions to the equator, inhabiting various zones of depths from the upper tidal limits to 50 fathoms; from the perfect manner in which specimens are preserved in the oldest tertiary beds; from the ease with which even a fragment of a valve can be recognised; from all these circumstances, I inferred that had sessile cirripedes existed during the secondary periods, they would certainly have been preserved and discovered; and as not one species had been discovered in beds of this age, I concluded that this great group had been suddenly developed at the commencement of the tertiary series. This was a sore trouble to me, adding as I thought one more instance of the abrupt appearance of a great group of species. But my work had hardly been published, when a skilful palaeontologist, M. Bosquet, sent me a drawing of a perfect specimen of an unmistakeable sessile cirripede, which he had himself extracted from the chalk of Belgium. And, as if to make the case as striking as possible, this sessile cirripede was a Chthamalus, a very common, large, and ubiquitous genus, of which not one specimen has as yet been found even in any tertiary stratum. Hence we now positively know that sessile cirripedes existed during the secondary period; and these cirripedes might have been the progenitors of our many tertiary and existing species.

The case most frequently insisted on by palaeontologists of the apparently sudden appearance of a whole group of species, is that of the teleostean fishes, low down in the chalk period. This group includes the large majority of existing species. Lately, Professor Pictet has carried their existence one sub-stage further back; and some palaeontologists believe that certain much older fishes, of which the affinities are as yet imperfectly known, are really teleostean. Assuming, however, that the whole of them did appear, as Agassiz believes, at the commencement of the chalk formation, the fact would certainly be highly remarkable; but I cannot see that it would be an insuperable difficulty on my theory, unless it could likewise be shown that the species of this group appeared suddenly and simultaneously throughout the world at this same period. It is almost superfluous to remark that hardly any fossil-fish are known from south of the equator; and by running through Pictet's Palaeontology it will be seen that very few species are known from several formations in Europe. Some few families of fish now have a confined range; the teleostean fish might formerly have had a similarly confined range, and after having been largely developed in some one sea, might have spread widely. Nor have we any right to suppose that the seas of the world have always been so freely open from south to north as they are at present. Even at this day, if the Malay Archipelago were converted into land, the tropical parts of the Indian Ocean would form a large and perfectly enclosed basin, in which any great group of marine animals might be multiplied; and here they would remain confined, until some of the species became adapted to a cooler climate, and were enabled to double the southern capes of Africa or Australia, and thus reach other and distant seas.

From these and similar considerations, but chiefly from our ignorance of the geology of other countries beyond the confines of Europe and the United States; and from the revolution in our palaeontological ideas on many points, which the discoveries of even the last dozen years have effected, it seems to me to be about as rash in us to dogmatize on the succession of organic beings throughout the world, as it would be for a naturalist to land for five minutes on some one barren point in Australia, and then to discuss the number and range of its productions.

On the sudden appearance of groups of Allied Species in the lowest known fossiliferous strata – There is another and allied difficulty, which is much graver. I allude to the manner in which numbers of species of the same group, suddenly appear in the lowest known fossiliferous rocks. Most of the arguments which have convinced me that all the existing species of the same group have descended from one progenitor, apply with nearly equal force to the earliest known species. For instance, I cannot doubt that all the Silurian trilobites have descended from some one crustacean, which must have lived long before the Silurian age, and which probably differed greatly from any known animal. Some of the most ancient Silurian animals, as the Nautilus, Lingula, &c., do not differ much from living species; and it cannot on my theory be supposed, that these old species were the progenitors of all the species of the orders to which they belong, for they do not present characters in any degree intermediate between them. If, moreover, they had been the progenitors of these orders, they would almost certainly have been long ago supplanted and exterminated by their numerous and improved descendants.

Consequently, if my theory be true, it is indisputable that before the lowest Silurian stratum was deposited, long periods elapsed, as long as, or probably far longer than, the whole interval from the Silurian age to the present day; and that during these vast, yet quite unknown, periods of time, the world swarmed with living creatures.

To the question why we do not find records of these vast primordial periods, I can give no satisfactory answer. Several of the most eminent geologists, with Sir R. Murchison at their head, are convinced that we see in the organic remains of the lowest Silurian stratum the dawn of life on this planet. Other highly competent judges, as Lyell and the late E. Forbes, dispute this conclusion. We should not forget that only a small portion of the world is known with accuracy. M. Barrande has lately added another and lower stage to the Silurian system, abounding with new and peculiar species. Traces of life have been detected in the Longmynd beds beneath Barrande's so-called primordial zone. The presence of phosphatic nodules and bituminous matter in some of the lowest azoic rocks, probably indicates the former existence of life at these periods. But the difficulty of understanding the absence of vast piles of fossiliferous strata, which on my theory no doubt were somewhere accumulated before the Silurian epoch, is very great. If these most ancient beds had been wholly worn away by denudation, or obliterated by metamorphic action, we ought to find only small remnants of the formations next succeeding them in age, and these ought to be very generally in a meta-morphosed condition. But the descriptions which we now possess of the Silurian deposits over immense territories in Russia and in North America, do not support the view, that the older a formation is, the more it has suffered the extremity of denudation and metamorphism.

The case at present must remain inexplicable; and may be truly urged as a valid argument against the views here entertained. To show that it may hereafter receive some explanation, I will give the following hypothesis. From the nature of the organic remains, which do not appear to have inhabited profound depths, in the several formations of Europe and of the United States; and from the amount of sediment, miles in thickness, of which the formations are composed, we may infer that from first to last large islands or tracts of land, whence the sediment was derived, occurred in the neighbourhood of the existing continents of Europe and North America. But we do not know what was the state of things in the intervals between the successive formations; whether Europe and the United States during these intervals existed as dry land, or as a submarine surface near land, on which sediment was not deposited, or again as the bed of an open and unfathomable sea.

Looking to the existing oceans, which are thrice as extensive as the land, we see them studded with many islands; but not one oceanic island is as yet known to afford even a remnant of any palaeozoic or secondary formation. Hence we may perhaps infer, that during the palaeozoic and secondary periods, neither continents nor continental islands existed where our oceans now extend;

for had they existed there, palaeozoic and secondary formations would in all probability have been accumulated from sediment derived from their wear and tear; and would have been at least partially upheaved by the oscillations of level, which we may fairly conclude must have intervened during these enormously long periods. If then we may infer anything from these facts, we may infer that where our oceans now extend, oceans have extended from the remotest period of which we have any record; and on the other hand, that where continents now exist, large tracts of land have existed, subjected no doubt to great oscillations of level, since the earliest silurian period. The coloured map appended to my volume on Coral Reefs, led me to conclude that the great oceans are still mainly areas of subsidence, the great archipelagoes still areas of oscillations of level, and the continents areas of elevation. But have we any right to assume that things have thus remained from eternity? Our continents seem to have been formed by a preponderance, during many oscillations of level, of the force of elevation; but may not the areas of preponderant movement have changed in the lapse of ages? At a period immeasurably antecedent to the silurian epoch, continents may have existed where oceans are now spread out; and clear and open oceans may have existed where our continents now stand. Nor should we be justified in assuming that if, for instance, the bed of the Pacific Ocean were now converted into a continent, we should there find formations older than the silurian strata, supposing such to have been formerly deposited; for it might well happen that strata which had subsided some miles nearer to the centre of the earth, and which had been pressed on by an enormous weight of superincumbent water, might have undergone far more metamorphic action than strata which have always remained nearer to the surface. The immense areas in some parts of the world, for instance in South America, of bare metamorphic rocks, which must have been heated under great pressure, have always seemed to me to require some special explanation; and we may perhaps believe that we see in these large areas, the many formations long anterior to the silurian epoch in a completely metamorphosed condition.

The several difficulties here discussed, namely our not finding in the successive formations infinitely numerous transitional links between the many species which now exist or have existed; the sudden manner in which whole groups of species appear in our European formations; the almost entire absence, as at present known, of fossiliferous formations beneath the Silurian strata, are all undoubtedly of the gravest nature. We see this in the plainest manner by the fact that all the most eminent palaeontologists, namely Cuvier, Owen, Agassiz, Barrande, Falconer, E. Forbes, &c., and all our greatest geologists, as Lyell, Murchison, Sedgwick, &c., have unanimously, often vehemently, maintained the immutability of species. But I have reason to believe that one great authority, Sir Charles Lyell, from further reflexion entertains grave doubts on this subject. I feel how rash it is to differ from these great authorities, to whom, with others, we owe all our knowledge. Those who think the natural geological record in any degree perfect, and who do not attach much weight to the facts and arguments of other kinds given in this volume, will undoubtedly at once reject my theory. For my part, following out Lyell's metaphor, I look at the natural geological record, as a history of the world imperfectly kept, and written in a changing dialect; of this history we possess the last volume alone, relating only to two or three countries. Of this volume, only here and there a short chapter has been preserved; and of each page, only here and there a few lines. Each word of the slowly-changing language, in which the history is supposed to be written, being more or less different in the interrupted succession of chapters, may represent the apparently abruptly changed forms of life, entombed in our consecutive, but widely separated, formations. On this view, the difficulties above discussed are greatly diminished, or even disappear.

On the Geological Succession
of Organic Beings

Let us now see whether the several facts and rules relating to the geological succession of organic beings, better accord with the common view of the immutability of species, or with that of their slow and gradual modification, through descent and natural selection.

New species have appeared very slowly, one after another, both on the land and in the waters. Lyell has shown that it is hardly possible to resist the evidence on this head in the case of the several tertiary stages; and every year tends to fill up the blanks between them, and to make the percentage system of lost and new forms more gradual. In some of the most recent beds, though undoubtedly of high antiquity if measured by years, only one or two species are lost forms, and only one or two are new forms, having here appeared for the first time, either locally, or, as far as we know, on the face of the earth. If we may trust the observations of Philippi in Sicily, the successive changes in the marine inhabitants of that island have been many and most gradual. The secondary formations are more broken; but, as Bronn has remarked, neither the appearance nor disappearance of their many now extinct species has been simultaneous in each separate formation.

Species of different genera and classes have not changed at the same rate, or in the same degree. In the oldest tertiary beds a few living shells may still be found in the midst of a multitude of extinct forms. Falconer has given a striking instance of a similar fact, in an existing crocodile associated with many strange and lost mammals and reptiles in the sub-Himalayan deposits. The Silurian Lingula differs but little from the living species of this genus; whereas most of the other Silurian Molluscs and all the Crustaceans have changed greatly. The productions of the land seem to change at a quicker rate than those of the sea, of which a striking instance has lately been observed in Switzerland. There is some reason to believe that organisms, considered high in the scale of nature, change more quickly than those that are low: though there are exceptions to this rule. The amount of organic change, as Pictet has remarked, does not strictly correspond with the succession of our geological formations; so that between each two consecutive formations, the forms of life have seldom changed in exactly the same degree. Yet if we compare any but the most closely related formations, all the species will be found to have undergone some change. When a species has once disappeared from the face of the earth, we have reason to believe that the same identical form never reappears. The strongest apparent exception to this latter rule, is that of the so-called 'colonies' of M. Barrande, which intrude for a period in the midst of an older formation, and then allow the pre-existing fauna to reappear; but Lyell's explanation, namely, that it is a case of temporary migration from a distinct geographical province, seems to me satisfactory.

These several facts accord well with my theory. I believe in no fixed law of development, causing all the inhabitants of a country to change abruptly, or simultaneously, or to an equal degree. The process of modification must be extremely slow. The variability of each species is quite independent of that of all others. Whether such variability be taken advantage of by natural selection, and whether the variations be accumulated to a greater or lesser amount, thus causing a greater or lesser amount of modification in the varying species, depends on many complex contingencies – on the variability being of a beneficial nature, on the power of intercrossing, on the rate of breeding, on the slowly changing physical conditions of the country, and more especially on the nature of the other inhabitants with which the varying species comes into competition. Hence it is by no means surprising that one species should retain the same identical form much longer than others; or, if changing, that it should change less. We see the same fact in geographical distribution; for instance, in the land-shells and coleopterous insects of Madeira having come to differ considerably from their nearest allies on the continent of Europe, whereas the marine shells and birds have remained unaltered. We can perhaps understand the apparently quicker rate of change in terrestrial and in more highly organised productions compared with marine and lower productions, by the more complex relations of the higher beings to their organic and inorganic conditions of life, as explained in a former chapter. When many of the inhabitants of a country have become modified and improved, we can understand, on the principle of competition, and on that of the many all-important relations of organism to organism, that any form which does not become in some degree modified and improved, will be liable to be exterminated. Hence we can see why all the species in the same region do at last, if we look to wide enough intervals of time, become modified; for those which do not change will become extinct.

In members of the same class the average amount of change, during long and equal periods of time, may, perhaps, be nearly the same; but as the accumulation of long-enduring fossiliferous formations depends on great masses of sediment having been deposited on areas whilst subsiding, our formations have been almost necessarily accumulated at wide and irregularly intermittent intervals; consequently the amount of organic change exhibited by the fossils embedded in consecutive formations is not equal. Each formation, on this view, does not mark a new and complete act of creation, but only an occasional scene, taken almost at hazard, in a slowly changing drama.

We can clearly understand why a species when once lost should never reappear, even if the very same conditions of life, organic and inorganic, should recur. For though the offspring of one species might be adapted (and no doubt this has occurred in innumerable instances) to fill the exact place of another species in the economy of nature, and thus supplant it; yet the two forms – the old and the new – would not be identically the same; for both would almost certainly inherit different characters from their distinct progenitors. For instance, it is just possible, if our fantail-pigeons were all destroyed, that fanciers, by striving during long ages for the same object, might make a new breed hardly distinguishable from our present fantail; but if the parent rock-pigeon were also destroyed, and in nature we have every reason to believe that the parent-form will generally be supplanted and exterminated by its improved offspring, it is quite incredible that a fantail, identical with the existing breed, could be raised from any other species of pigeon, or even from the other well-established races of the domestic pigeon, for the newly-formed fantail would be almost sure to inherit from its new progenitor some slight characteristic differences.

Groups of species, that is, genera and families, follow the same general rules in their appearance and disappearance as do single species, changing more or less quickly, and in a greater or lesser degree. A group does not reappear after it has once disappeared; or its existence, as long as it lasts, is continuous. I am aware that there are some apparent exceptions to this rule, but the exceptions are surprisingly few, so few, that E. Forbes, Pictet, and Woodward (though all strongly opposed to such views as I maintain) admit its truth; and the rule strictly accords with my theory. For as all the species of the same group have descended from some one species, it is clear that as long as any species of the group have appeared in the long succession of ages, so long must its members have continuously existed, in order to have generated either new and modified or the same old and unmodified forms. Species of the genus Lingula, for instance, must have continuously existed by an unbroken succession of generations, from the lowest Silurian stratum to the present day.

We have seen in the last chapter that the species of a group sometimes falsely appear to have come in abruptly;

and I have attempted to give an explanation of this fact, which if true would have been fatal to my views. But such cases are certainly exceptional; the general rule being a gradual increase in number, till the group reaches its maximum, and then, sooner or later, it gradually decreases. If the number of the species of a genus, or the number of the genera of a family, be represented by a vertical line of varying thickness, crossing the successive geological formations in which the species are found, the line will sometimes falsely appear to begin at its lower end, not in a sharp point, but abruptly; it then gradually thickens upwards, sometimes keeping for a space of equal thickness, and ultimately thins out in the upper beds, marking the decrease and final extinction of the species. This gradual increase in number of the species of a group is strictly conformable with my theory; as the species of the same genus, and the genera of the same family, can increase only slowly and progressively; for the process of modification and the production of a number of allied forms must be slow and gradual – one species giving rise first to two or three varieties, these being slowly converted into species, which in their turn produce by equally slow steps other species, and so on, like the branching of a great tree from a single stem, till the group becomes large.

On Extinction – We have as yet spoken only incidentally of the disappearance of species and of groups of species. On the theory of natural selection the extinction of old forms and the production of new and improved forms are intimately connected together. The old notion of all the inhabitants of the earth having been swept away at successive periods by catastrophes, is very generally given up, even by those geologists, as Elie de Beaumont, Murchison, Barrande, &c., whose general views would naturally lead them to this conclusion. On the contrary, we have every reason to believe, from the study of the tertiary formations, that species and groups of species gradually disappear, one after another, first from one spot, then from another, and finally from the world. Both single species and whole groups of species last for very unequal periods; some groups, as we have seen, having endured from the earliest known dawn of life to the present day; some having disappeared before the close of the palaeozoic period. No fixed law seems to determine the length of time during which any single species or any single genus endures. There is reason to believe that the complete extinction of the species of a group is generally a slower process than their production: if the appearance and disappearance of a group of species be represented, as before, by a vertical line of varying thickness, the line is found to taper more gradually at its upper end, which marks the progress of extermination, than at its lower end, which marks the first appearance and increase in numbers of the species. In some cases, however, the extermination of whole groups of beings, as of ammonites towards the close of the secondary period, has been wonderfully sudden.

The whole subject of the extinction of species has been involved in the most gratuitous mystery. Some authors have even supposed that as the individual has a definite length of life, so have species a definite duration.

No one I think can have marvelled more at the extinction of species, than I have done. When I found in La Plata the tooth of a horse embedded with the remains of Mastodon, Megatherium, Toxodon, and other extinct monsters, which all coexisted with still living shells at a very late geological period, I was filled with astonishment; for seeing that the horse, since its introduction by the Spaniards into South America, has run wild over the whole country and has increased in numbers at an unparalleled rate, I asked myself what could so recently have exterminated the former horse under conditions of life apparently so favourable. But how utterly groundless was my astonishment! Professor Owen soon perceived that the tooth, though so like that of the existing horse, belonged to an extinct species. Had this horse been still living, but in some degree rare, no naturalist would have felt the least surprise at its rarity; for rarity is the attribute of a vast number of species of all classes, in all countries. If we ask ourselves why this or that species is rare, we answer that something is unfavourable in its conditions of life; but what that something is, we can hardly ever tell. On the supposition of the fossil horse still existing as a rare species, we might have felt certain from the analogy of all other mammals, even of the slow-breeding elephant, and from the history of the naturalisation of the domestic horse in South America, that under more favourable conditions it would in a very few years have stocked the whole continent. But we could not have told what the unfavourable conditions were which checked its increase, whether some one or several contingencies, and at what period of the horse's life, and in what degree, they severally acted.

If the conditions had gone on, however slowly, becoming less and less favourable, we assuredly should not have perceived the fact, yet the fossil horse would certainly have become rarer and rarer, and finally extinct; – its place being seized on by some more successful competitor.

It is most difficult always to remember that the increase of every living being is constantly being checked by unperceived injurious agencies; and that these same unperceived agencies are amply sufficient to cause rarity, and finally extinction. We see in many cases in the more recent tertiary formations, that rarity precedes extinction; and we know that this has been the progress of events with those animals which have been exterminated, either locally or wholly, through man's agency. I may repeat what I published in 1845, namely, that to admit that species generally become rare before they become extinct – to feel no surprise at the rarity of a species, and yet to marvel greatly when it ceases to exist, is much the same as to admit that sickness in the individual is the forerunner of death – to feel no surprise at sickness, but when the sick man dies, to wonder and to suspect that he died by some unknown deed of violence.

The theory of natural selection is grounded on the belief that each new variety, and ultimately each new species, is produced and maintained by having some advantage over those with which it comes into competition; and the consequent extinction of less-favoured forms almost inevitably follows. It is the same with our domestic productions: when a new and slightly improved variety has been raised, it at first supplants the less improved varieties in the same neighbourhood; when much improved it is transported far and near, like our short-horn cattle, and takes the place of other breeds in other countries. Thus the appearance of new forms and the disappearance of old forms, both natural and artificial, are bound together. In certain flourishing groups, the number of new specific forms which have been produced within a given time is probably greater than that of the old forms which have been exterminated; but we know that the number of species has not gone on indefinitely increasing, at least during the later geological periods, so that looking to later times we may believe that the production of new forms has caused the extinction of about the same number of old forms.

The competition will generally be most severe, as formerly explained and illustrated by examples, between the forms which are most like each other in all respects. Hence the improved and modified descendants of a species will generally cause the extermination of the parent-species; and if many new forms have been developed from any one species, the nearest allies of that species, *i. e.* the species of the same genus, will be the most liable to extermination. Thus, as I believe, a number of new species descended from one species, that is a new genus, comes to supplant an old genus, belonging to the same family. But it must often have happened that a new species belonging to some one group will have seized on the place occupied by a species belonging to a distinct group, and thus caused its extermination; and if many allied forms be developed from the successful intruder, many will have to yield their places; and it will generally be allied forms, which will suffer from some inherited inferiority in common. But whether it be species belonging to the same or to a distinct class, which yield their places to other species which have been modified and improved, a few of the sufferers may often long be preserved, from being fitted to some peculiar line of life, or from inhabiting some distant and isolated station, where they have escaped severe competition. For instance, a single species of Trigonia, a great genus of shells in the secondary formations, survives in the Australian seas; and a few members of the great and almost extinct group of Ganoid fishes still inhabit our fresh waters. Therefore the utter extinction of a group is generally, as we have seen, a slower process than its production.

With respect to the apparently sudden extermination of whole families or orders, as of Trilobites at the close of the palaeozoic period and of Ammonites at the close of the secondary period, we must remember what has been already said on the probable wide intervals of time between our consecutive formations; and in these intervals there may have been much slow extermination. Moreover, when by sudden immigration or by unusually rapid development, many species of a new group have taken possession of a new area, they will have exterminated in a correspondingly rapid manner many of the old inhabitants; and the forms which thus yield their places will commonly be allied, for they will partake of some inferiority in common.

Thus, as it seems to me, the manner in which single species and whole groups of species become extinct, accords well with the theory of natural selection. We need not marvel at extinction; if we must marvel, let it be at our presumption in imagining for a moment that we understand the many complex contingencies, on which the existence of each species depends. If we forget for an instant, that each species tends to increase inordinately, and that some check is always in action, yet seldom perceived by us, the whole economy of nature will be utterly obscured. Whenever we can precisely say why this species is more abundant in individuals than that; why this species and not another can be naturalised in a given country; then, and not till then, we may justly feel surprise why we cannot account for the extinction of this particular species or group of species.

On the Forms of Life changing almost simultaneously throughout the World – Scarcely any palaeontological discovery is more striking than the fact, that the forms of life change almost simultaneously throughout the world. Thus our European Chalk formation can be recognised in many distant parts of the world, under the most different climates, where not a fragment of the mineral chalk itself can be found; namely, in North America, in equatorial South America, in Tierra del Fuego, at the Cape of Good Hope, and in the peninsula of India. For at these distant points, the organic remains in certain beds present an unmistakeable degree of resemblance to those of the Chalk. It is not that the same species are met with; for in some cases not one species is identically the same, but they belong to the same families, genera, and sections of genera, and sometimes are similarly characterised in such trifling points as mere superficial sculpture. Moreover other forms, which are not found in the Chalk of Europe, but which occur in the formations either above or below, are similarly absent at these distant points of the world. In the several successive palaeozoic formations of Russia, Western Europe and North America, a similar parallelism in the forms of life has been observed by several authors: so it is, according to Lyell, with the several European and North American tertiary deposits. Even if the few fossil species which are common to the Old and New Worlds be kept wholly out of view, the general parallelism in the successive forms of life, in the stages of the widely separated palaeozoic and tertiary periods, would still be manifest, and the several formations could be easily correlated.

These observations, however, relate to the marine inhabitants of distant parts of the world: we have not sufficient data to judge whether the productions of the land and of fresh water change at distant points in the same parallel manner. We may doubt whether they have thus changed: if the Megatherium, Mylodon, Macrauchenia, and Toxodon had been brought to Europe from La Plata, without any information in regard to their geological position, no one would have suspected that they had coexisted with still living sea-shells; but as these anomalous monsters coexisted with the Mastodon and Horse, it might at least have been inferred that they had lived during one of the later tertiary stages.

When the marine forms of life are spoken of as having changed simultaneously throughout the world, it must not be supposed that this expression relates to the same thousandth or hundred-thousandth year, or even that it has a very strict geological sense; for if all the marine animals which live at the present day in Europe, and all those that lived in Europe during the pleistocene period (an enormously remote period as measured by years, including the whole Glacial epoch), were to be compared with those now living in South America or in Australia, the most skilful naturalist would hardly be able to say whether the existing or the pleistocene inhabitants of Europe resembled most closely those of the southern hemisphere. So, again, several highly competent observers believe that the existing productions of the United States are more closely related to those which lived in Europe during certain later tertiary stages, than to those which now live here; and if this be so, it is evident that fossiliferous beds deposited at the present day on the shores of North America would hereafter be liable to be classed with somewhat older European beds. Nevertheless, looking to a remotely future epoch, there can, I think, be little doubt that all the more modern *marine* formations, namely, the upper pliocene, the pleistocene and strictly modern beds, of Europe, North and South America, and Australia, from containing fossil remains in some degree allied, and from not including those forms which are only found in the older underlying deposits, would be correctly ranked as simultaneous in a geological sense.

The fact of the forms of life changing simultaneously, in the above large sense, at distant parts of the world, has greatly struck those admirable observers, MM. de Verneuil and d'Archiac. After referring to the parallelism of the palaeozoic forms of life in various parts of Europe, they add, 'If struck by this strange sequence, we turn our attention to North America, and there discover a series of analogous phenomena, it will appear certain that all these modifications of species, their extinction, and the introduction of new ones, cannot be owing to mere changes in marine currents or other causes more or less local and temporary, but depend on general laws which govern the whole animal kingdom.' M. Barrande has made forcible remarks to precisely the same effect. It is, indeed, quite futile to look to changes of currents, climate, or other physical conditions, as the cause of these great mutations in the forms of life throughout the world, under the most different climates. We must, as Barrande has remarked, look to some special law. We shall see this more clearly when we treat of the present distribution of organic beings, and find how slight is the relation between the physical conditions of various countries, and the nature of their inhabitants.

This great fact of the parallel succession of the forms of life throughout the world, is explicable on the theory of natural selection. New species are formed by new varieties arising, which have some advantage over older forms; and those forms, which are already dominant, or have some advantage over the other forms in their own country, would naturally oftenest give rise to new varieties or incipient species; for these latter must be victorious in a still higher degree in order to be preserved and to survive. We have distinct evidence on this head, in the plants which are dominant, that is, which are commonest in their own homes, and are most widely diffused, having produced the greatest number of new varieties. It is also natural that the dominant, varying, and far-spreading species, which already have invaded to a certain extent the territories of other species, should be those which would have the best chance of spreading still further, and of giving rise in new countries to new varieties and species. The process of diffusion may often be very slow, being dependent on climatal and geographical changes, or on strange accidents, but in the long run the dominant forms will generally succeed in spreading. The diffusion would, it is probable, be slower with the terrestrial inhabitants of distinct continents than with the marine inhabitants of the continuous sea. We might therefore expect to find, as we apparently do find, a less strict degree of parallel succession in the productions of the land than of the sea.

Dominant species spreading from any region might encounter still more dominant species, and then their triumphant course, or even their existence, would cease. We know not at all precisely what are all the conditions most favourable for the multiplication of new and dominant species; but we can, I think, clearly see that a number of individuals, from giving a better chance of the appearance of favourable variations, and that severe competition with many already existing forms, would be highly favourable, as would be the power of spreading into new territories. A certain amount of isolation, recurring at long intervals of time, would probably be also favourable, as before explained. One quarter of the world may have been most favourable for the production of new and dominant species on the land, and another for those in the waters of the sea. If two great regions had been for a long period favourably circumstanced in an equal degree, whenever their inhabitants met, the battle would be prolonged and severe; and some from one birthplace and some from the other might be victorious. But in the course of time, the forms dominant in the highest degree, wherever produced, would tend everywhere to prevail. As they prevailed, they would cause the extinction of other and inferior forms; and as these inferior forms would be allied in groups by inheritance, whole groups would tend slowly to disappear: though here and there a single member might long be enabled to survive.

Thus, as it seems to me, the parallel, and, taken in a large sense, simultaneous, succession of the same forms of life throughout the world, accords well with the principle of new species having been formed by dominant species spreading widely and varying; the new species thus produced being themselves dominant owing to inheritance, and to having already had some advantage over their parents or over other species; these again spreading, varying, and producing new species. The forms which are beaten and which yield their places to the new and victorious forms, will generally be allied in groups, from inheriting some inferiority in common; and therefore as new and improved groups spread throughout the world, old groups will disappear from the world; and the succession of forms in both ways will everywhere tend to correspond.

There is one other remark connected with this subject worth making. I have given my reasons for believing that all our greater fossiliferous formations were deposited during periods of subsidence; and that blank intervals of vast duration occurred during the periods when the bed of the sea was either stationary or rising, and likewise when sediment was not thrown down quickly enough to embed and preserve organic remains. During these long and blank intervals I suppose that the inhabitants of each region underwent a considerable amount of modification and extinction, and that there was much migration from other parts of the world. As we have reason to believe that large areas are affected by the same movement, it is probable that strictly contemporaneous formations have often been accumulated over very wide spaces in the same quarter of the world; but we are far from having any right to conclude that this has invariably been the case, and that large areas have invariably been affected by the same movements. When two formations have been deposited in two regions during nearly, but not exactly the same period, we should find in both, from the causes explained in the foregoing paragraphs, the same general succession in the forms of life; but the species would not exactly correspond; for there will have been a little more time in the one region than in the other for modification, extinction, and immigration.

I suspect that cases of this nature have occurred in Europe. Mr Prestwich, in his admirable Memoirs on the eocene deposits of England and France, is able to draw a close general parallelism between the successive stages in the two countries; but when he compares certain stages in England with those in France, although he finds in both a curious accordance in the numbers of the species belonging to the same genera, yet the species themselves differ in a manner very difficult to account for, considering the proximity of the two areas – unless, indeed, it be assumed that an isthmus separated two seas inhabited by distinct, but contemporaneous, faunas. Lyell has made similar observations on some of the later tertiary formations. Barrande, also, shows that there is a striking general parallelism in the successive Silurian deposits of Bohemia and Scandinavia; nevertheless he finds a surprising amount of difference in the species. If the several formations in these regions have not been deposited during the same exact periods – a formation in one region often corresponding with a blank interval in the other – and if in both regions the species have gone on slowly changing during the accumulation of the several formations and during the long intervals of time between them; in this case, the several formations in the two regions could be arranged in the same order, in accordance with the general succession of the form of life, and the order would falsely appear to be strictly parallel; nevertheless the species would not all be the same in the apparently corresponding stages in the two regions.

On the Affinities of extinct Species to each other, and to living forms – Let us now look to the mutual affinities of extinct and living species. They all fall into one grand natural system; and this fact is at once explained on the principle of descent. The more ancient any form is, the more, as a general rule, it differs from living forms. But, as Buckland long ago remarked, all fossils can be classed either in still existing groups, or between them. That the extinct forms of life help to fill up the wide intervals between existing genera, families, and orders, cannot be disputed. For if we confine our attention either to the living or to the extinct alone, the series is far less perfect than if we combine both into one general system. With respect to the Vertebrata, whole pages could be filled with striking illustrations from our great palaeontologist, Owen, showing how extinct animals fall in between existing groups. Cuvier ranked the Ruminants and Pachyderms, as the two most distinct orders of mammals; but Owen has discovered so many fossil links, that he has had to alter the whole classification of these two orders; and has placed certain pachyderms in the same sub-order with ruminants: for example, he dissolves by fine gradations the apparently wide difference between the pig and the camel. In regard to the Invertebrata, Barrande, and a higher authority could not be named, asserts that he is every day taught that palaeozoic animals, though belonging to the same orders, families, or genera with those living at the present day, were not at this early epoch limited in such distinct groups as they now are.

Some writers have objected to any extinct species or group of species being considered as intermediate between living species or groups. If by this term it is meant that an extinct form is directly intermediate in all its characters between two living forms, the objection is probably valid. But I apprehend that in a perfectly natural classification many fossil species would have to stand between living species, and some extinct genera between living genera, even between genera belonging to distinct families. The most common case, especially with respect to very distinct groups, such as fish and reptiles, seems to be, that supposing them to be distinguished at the present day from each other by a dozen characters, the ancient members of the same two groups would be distinguished by a somewhat lesser number of characters, so that the two groups, though formerly quite distinct, at that period made some small approach to each other.

It is a common belief that the more ancient a form is, by so much the more it tends to connect by some of its characters groups now widely separated from each other. This remark no doubt must be restricted to those groups which have undergone much change in the course of geological ages; and it would be difficult to prove the truth of the proposition, for every now and then even a living animal, as the Lepidosiren, is discovered having affinities directed towards very distinct groups. Yet if we compare the older Reptiles and Batrachians, the older Fish, the older Cephalopods, and the eocene Mammals, with the more recent members of the same classes, we must admit that there is some truth in the remark.

Let us see how far these several facts and inferences accord with the theory of descent with modification. As the subject is somewhat complex, I must request the reader to turn to the diagram in the fourth chapter [see p vi of this edition]. We may suppose that the numbered letters represent genera, and the dotted lines diverging from them the species in each genus. The diagram is much too simple, too few genera and too few species being given, but this is unimportant for us. The horizontal lines may represent successive geological formations, and all the forms beneath the uppermost line may be considered as extinct. The three existing genera, a^{14}, q^{14}, p^{14}, will form a small family; b^{14} and f^{14} a closely allied family or sub-family; and o^{14}, e^{14}, m^{14}, a third family. These three families, together with the many extinct genera on the several lines of descent diverging from the parent-form A, will form an order; for all will have inherited something in common from their ancient and common progenitor. On the principle of the continued tendency to divergence of character, which was formerly illustrated by this diagram, the more recent any form is, the more it will generally differ from its ancient progenitor. Hence we can understand the rule that the most ancient fossils differ most from existing forms. We must not, however, assume that divergence of character is a necessary contingency; it depends solely on the descendants from a species being thus enabled to seize on many and different places in the economy of nature. Therefore it is quite possible, as we have seen in the case of some Silurian forms, that a species might go on being slightly modified in relation to its slightly altered conditions of life, and yet retain throughout a vast period the same general characteristics. This is represented in the diagram by the letter F^{14}.

All the many forms, extinct and recent, descended from A, make, as before remarked, one order; and this order, from the continued effects of extinction and divergence of character, has become divided into several sub-families and families, some of which are supposed to have perished at different periods, and some to have endured to the present day.

By looking at the diagram we can see that if many of the extinct forms, supposed to be embedded in the successive formations, were discovered at several points low down in the series, the three existing families on the uppermost line would be rendered less distinct from each other. If, for instance, the genera a^1, a^5, a^{10}, f^8, m^3, m^6, m^9 were disinterred, these three families would be so closely linked together that they probably would have to be united into one great family, in nearly the same manner as has occurred with ruminants and pachyderms. Yet he who objected to call the extinct genera, which thus linked the living genera of three families together, intermediate in character, would be justified, as they are intermediate, not directly, but only by a long and circuitous course through many widely different forms. If many extinct forms were to be discovered above one of the middle horizontal lines or geological formations – for instance, above No. VI – but none from beneath this line, then only the two families on the left hand (namely, a^{14}, &c., and b^{14}, &c.) would have to be united into one family; and the two other families (namely, a^{14} to f^{14} now including five genera, and o^{14} to m^{14}) would yet remain distinct. These two families, however, would be less distinct from each other than they were before the discovery of the fossils. If, for instance, we suppose the existing genera of the two families to differ from each other by a dozen characters, in this case the genera, at the early period marked VI, would differ by a lesser number of characters; for at this early stage of descent they have not diverged in character from the common progenitor of the order, nearly so much as they subsequently diverged. Thus it comes that ancient and extinct genera are often in some slight degree intermediate in character between their modified descendants, or between their collateral relations.

In nature the case will be far more complicated than is represented in the diagram; for the groups will have been more numerous, they will have endured for extremely unequal lengths of time, and will have been modified in various degrees. As we possess only the last volume of the geological record, and that in a very broken condition, we have no right to expect, except in very rare cases, to fill up wide intervals in the natural system, and thus unite distinct families or orders. All that we have a right to expect, is that those groups, which have within known geological periods undergone much modification, should in the older formations make some slight approach to each other; so that the older members should differ less from each other in some of their characters than do the existing members of the same groups; and this by the concurrent evidence of our best palaeontologists seems frequently to be the case.

Thus, on the theory of descent with modification, the main facts with respect to the mutual affinities of the extinct forms of life to each other and to living forms, seem to me explained in a satisfactory manner. And they are wholly inexplicable on any other view.

On this same theory, it is evident that the fauna of any great period in the earth's history will be intermediate in general character between that which preceded and that which succeeded it. Thus, the species which lived at the sixth great stage of descent in the diagram are the modified offspring of those which lived at the fifth stage, and are the parents of those which became still more modified at the seventh stage; hence they could hardly fail to be nearly intermediate in character between the forms of life above and below. We must, however, allow for the entire extinction of some preceding forms, and for the coming in of quite new forms by immigration, and for a large amount of modification, during the long and blank intervals between the successive formations. Subject to these allowances, the fauna of each geological period undoubtedly is intermediate in character, between the preceding and succeeding faunas. I need give only one instance, namely, the manner in which the fossils of the Devonian system, when this system was first discovered, were at once recognised by palaeontologists as intermediate in character between those of the overlying carboniferous, and underlying Silurian system. But each fauna is not necessarily exactly intermediate, as unequal intervals of time have elapsed between consecutive formations.

It is no real objection to the truth of the statement, that the fauna of each period as a whole is nearly intermediate in character between the preceding and succeeding faunas, that certain genera offer exceptions to the rule. For instance, mastodons and elephants, when arranged by Dr Falconer in two series, first according to their mutual affinities and then according to their periods of existence, do not accord in arrangement. The species extreme in character are not the oldest, or the most recent; nor are those which are intermediate in character, intermediate in age. But supposing for an instant, in this and other such cases, that the record of the first appearance and disappearance of the species was perfect, we have no reason to believe that forms successively produced necessarily endure for corresponding lengths of time: a very ancient form might occasionally last much longer than a form elsewhere subsequently produced, especially in the case of terrestrial productions inhabiting separated districts. To compare small things with great: if the principal living and extinct races of the domestic pigeon were arranged as well as they could be in serial affinity, this arrangement would not closely accord with the order in time of their production, and still less with the order of their disappearance; for the parent rock-pigeon now lives; and many varieties between the rock-pigeon and the carrier have become extinct; and carriers which are extreme in the important character of length of beak originated earlier than short-beaked tumblers, which are at the opposite end of the series in this same respect.

Closely connected with the statement, that the organic remains from an intermediate formation are in some degree intermediate in character, is the fact, insisted on by all palaeontologists, that fossils from two consecutive formations are far more closely related to each other, than are the fossils from two remote formations. Pictet gives as a well-known instance, the general resemblance of the organic remains from the several stages of the Chalk formation, though the species are distinct in each stage. This fact alone, from its generality, seems to have shaken Professor Pictet in his firm belief in the immutability of species. He who is acquainted with the distribution of existing species over the globe, will not attempt to account for the close resemblance of the distinct species in closely consecutive formations, by the physical conditions of the ancient areas having remained nearly the same. Let it be remembered that the forms of life, at least those inhabiting the sea, have changed almost simultaneously throughout the world, and therefore under the most different climates and conditions. Consider the prodigious vicissitudes of climate during the pleistocene period, which includes the whole Glacial period, and note how little the specific forms of the inhabitants of the sea have been affected.

On the theory of descent, the full meaning of the fact of fossil remains from closely consecutive formations, though ranked as distinct species, being closely related, is obvious. As the accumulation of each formation has often been interrupted, and as long blank intervals have intervened between successive formations, we ought not to expect to find, as I attempted to show in the last chapter, in any one or two formations all the intermediate varieties between the species which appeared at the commencement and close of these periods; but we ought to find after intervals, very long as measured by years, but only moderately long as measured geologically, closely allied forms, or, as they have been called by some authors, representative species; and these we assuredly do find. We find, in short, such evidence of the slow and scarcely sensible mutation of specific forms, as we have a just right to expect to find.

On the state of Development of Ancient Forms – There has been much discussion whether recent forms are more highly developed than ancient. I will not here enter on this subject, for naturalists have not as yet defined to each other's satisfaction what is meant by high and low forms. But in one particular sense the more recent forms must, on my theory, be higher than the more ancient; for each new species is formed by having had some advantage in the struggle for life over other and preceding forms. If under a nearly similar climate, the eocene inhabitants of one quarter of the world were put into competition with the existing inhabitants of the same or some other quarter, the eocene fauna or flora would certainly be beaten and exterminated; as would a secondary fauna by an eocene, and a palaeozoic fauna by a secondary fauna. I do not doubt that this process of improvement has affected in a marked and sensible manner the organisation of the more recent and victorious forms of life, in comparison with the ancient and beaten forms; but I can see no way of testing this sort of progress. Crustaceans, for instance, not the highest in their own class, may have beaten the highest molluscs. From the extraordinary manner in which European productions have recently spread over New Zealand, and have seized on places which must have been previously occupied, we may believe, if all the animals and plants of Great Britain were set free in New Zealand, that in the course of time a multitude of British forms would become thoroughly naturalized there, and would exterminate many of the natives. On the other hand, from what we see now occurring in New Zealand, and from hardly a single inhabitant of the southern hemisphere having become wild in any part of Europe, we may doubt, if all the productions of New Zealand were set free in Great Britain, whether any considerable number would be enabled to seize on places now occupied by our native plants and animals. Under this point of view, the productions of Great Britain may be said to be higher than those of New Zealand. Yet the most skilful naturalist from an examination of the species of the two countries could not have foreseen this result.

Agassiz insists that ancient animals resemble to a certain extent the embryos of recent animals of the same classes; or that the geological succession of extinct forms is in some degree parallel to the embryological development of recent forms. I must follow Pictet and Huxley in thinking that the truth of this doctrine is very far from proved. Yet I fully expect to see it hereafter confirmed, at least in regard to subordinate groups, which have branched off from each other within comparatively recent times. For this doctrine of Agassiz accords well with the theory of natural selection. In a future chapter I shall attempt to show that the adult differs from its embryo, owing to variations supervening at a not early age, and being inherited at a corresponding age. This process, whilst it leaves the embryo almost unaltered, continually adds, in the course of successive generations, more and more difference to the adult.

Thus the embryo comes to be left as a sort of picture, preserved by nature, of the ancient and less modified condition of each animal. This view may be true, and yet it may never be capable of full proof. Seeing, for instance, that the oldest known mammals, reptiles, and fish strictly belong to their own proper classes, though some of these old forms are in a slight degree less distinct from each other than are the typical members of the same groups at the present day, it would be vain to look for animals having the common embryological character of the Vertebrata, until beds far beneath the lowest Silurian strata are discovered – a discovery of which the chance is very small.

On the Succession of the same Types within the same areas, during the later tertiary periods – Mr Clift many years ago showed that the fossil mammals from the Australian caves were closely allied to the living marsupials of that continent. In South America, a similar relationship is manifest, even to an uneducated eye, in the gigantic pieces of armour like those of the armadillo, found in several parts of La Plata; and Professor Owen has shown in the most striking manner that most of the fossil mammals, buried there in such numbers, are related to South American types. This relationship is even more clearly seen in the wonderful collection of fossil bones made by MM. Lund and Clausen in the caves of Brazil. I was so much impressed with these facts that I strongly insisted, in 1839 and 1845, on this 'law of the succession of types' – on 'this wonderful relationship in the same continent between the dead and the living'. Professor Owen has subsequently extended the same generalisation to the mammals of the Old World. We see the same law in this author's restorations of the extinct and gigantic birds of New Zealand. We see it also in the birds of the caves of Brazil. Mr Woodward has shown that the same law holds good with sea-shells, but from the wide distribution of most genera of molluscs, it is not well displayed by them. Other cases could be added, as the relation between the extinct and living land-shells of Madeira; and between the extinct and living brackish-water shells of the Aralo-Caspian Sea.

Now what does this remarkable law of the succession of the same types within the same areas mean? He would be a bold man, who after comparing the present climate of Australia and of parts of South America under the same latitude, would attempt to account, on the one hand, by dissimilar physical conditions for the dissimilarity of the inhabitants of these two continents, and, on the other hand, by similarity of conditions, for the uniformity of the same types in each during the later tertiary periods. Nor can it be pretended that it is an immutable law that marsupials should have been chiefly or solely produced in Australia; or that Edentata and other American types should have been solely produced in South America. For we know that Europe in ancient times was peopled by numerous marsupials; and I have shown in the publications above alluded to, that in America the law of distribution of terrestrial mammals was formerly different from what it now is. North America formerly partook strongly of the present character of the southern half of the continent; and the southern half was formerly more closely allied, than it is at present, to the northern half. In a similar manner we know from Falconer and Cautley's discoveries, that northern India was formerly more closely related in its mammals to Africa than it is at the present time. Analogous facts could be given in relation to the distribution of marine animals.

On the theory of descent with modification, the great law of the long enduring, but not immutable, succession of the same types within the same areas, is at once explained; for the inhabitants of each quarter of the world will obviously tend to leave in that quarter, during the next succeeding period of time, closely allied though in some degree modified descendants. If the inhabitants of one continent formerly differed greatly from those of another continent, so will their modified descendants still differ in nearly the same manner and degree. But after very long intervals of time and after great geographical changes, permitting much inter-migration, the feebler will yield to the more dominant forms, and there will be nothing immutable in the laws of past and present distribution.

It may be asked in ridicule, whether I suppose that the megatherium and other allied huge monsters have left behind them in South America the sloth, armadillo, and anteater, as their degenerate descendants. This cannot for an instant be admitted. These huge animals have become wholly extinct, and have left no progeny. But in the caves of Brazil, there are many extinct species which are closely allied in size and in other characters to the species still living in South America; and some of these fossils may be the actual progenitors of living species. It must not be forgotten that, on my theory, all the species of the same genus have descended from some one species; so that if six genera, each having eight species, be found in one geological formation, and in the next succeeding formation there be six other allied or representative genera with the same number of species, then we may conclude that only one species of each of the six older genera has left modified descendants, constituting the six new genera. The other seven species of the old genera have all died out and have left no progeny. Or, which would probably be a far commoner case, two or three species of two or three alone of the six older genera will have been the parents of the six new genera; the other old species and the other whole genera having become utterly extinct. In failing orders, with the genera and species decreasing in numbers, as apparently is the case of the Edentata of South America, still fewer genera and species will have left modified blood-descendants.

Summary of the preceding and present Chapters – I have attempted to show that the geological record is extremely imperfect; that only a small portion of the globe has been geologically explored with care; that only certain classes of organic beings have been largely preserved in a fossil state; that the number both of specimens and of species, preserved in our museums, is absolutely as nothing compared with the incalculable number of generations which must have passed away even during a single formation; that, owing to subsidence being necessary for the accumulation of fossiliferous deposits thick enough to resist future degradation, enormous intervals of time have elapsed between the successive formations; that there has probably been more extinction during the periods of subsidence, and more variation during the periods of elevation, and during the latter the record will have been least perfectly kept; that each single formation has not been continuously deposited; that the duration of each formation is, perhaps, short compared with the average duration of specific forms; that migration has played an important part in the first appearance of new forms in any one area and formation; that widely ranging species are those which have varied most, and have oftenest given rise to new species; and that varieties have at first often been local. All these causes taken conjointly, must have tended to make the geological record extremely imperfect, and will to a large extent explain why we do not find interminable varieties, connecting together all the extinct and existing forms of life by the finest graduated steps.

He who rejects these views on the nature of the geological record, will rightly reject my whole theory. For he may ask in vain where are the numberless transitional links which must formerly have connected the closely allied or representative species, found in the several stages of the same great formation. He may disbelieve in the enormous intervals of time which have elapsed between our consecutive formations; he may overlook how important a part migration must have played, when the formations of any one great region alone, as that of Europe, are considered; he may urge the apparent, but often falsely apparent, sudden coming in of whole groups of species. He may ask where are the remains of those infinitely numerous organisms which must have existed long before the first bed of the Silurian system was deposited: I can answer this latter question only hypothetically, by saying that as far as we can see, where our oceans now extend they have for an enormous period extended, and where our oscillating continents now stand they have stood ever since the Silurian epoch; but that long before that period, the world may have presented a wholly different aspect; and that the older continents, formed of formations older than any known to us, may now all be in a metamorphosed condition, or may lie buried under the ocean.

Passing from these difficulties, all the other great leading facts in palaeontology seem to me simply to follow on the theory of descent with modification through natural selection. We can thus understand how it is that new species come in slowly and successively; how species of different classes do not necessarily change together, or at the same rate, or in the same degree; yet in the long run that all undergo modification to some extent. The extinction of old forms is the almost inevitable consequence of the production of new forms. We can understand why when a species has once disappeared it never reappears.

Groups of species increase in numbers slowly, and endure for unequal periods of time; for the process of modification is necessarily slow, and depends on many complex contingencies. The dominant species of the larger dominant groups tend to leave many modified descendants, and thus new sub-groups and groups are formed. As these are formed, the species of the less vigorous groups, from their inferiority inherited from a common progenitor, tend to become extinct together, and to leave no modified offspring on the face of the earth. But the utter extinction of a whole group of species may often be a very slow process, from the survival of a few descendants, lingering in protected and isolated situations. When a group has once wholly disappeared, it does not reappear; for the link of generation has been broken.

We can understand how the spreading of the dominant forms of life, which are those that oftenest vary, will in the long run tend to people the world with allied, but modified, descendants; and these will generally succeed in taking the places of those groups of species which are their inferiors in the struggle for existence. Hence, after long intervals of time, the productions of the world will appear to have changed simultaneously.

We can understand how it is that all the forms of life, ancient and recent, make together one grand system; for all are connected by generation. We can understand, from the continued tendency to divergence of character, why the more ancient a form is, the more it generally differs from those now living. Why ancient and extinct forms often tend to fill up gaps between existing forms, sometimes blending two groups previously classed as distinct into one; but more commonly only bringing them a little closer together. The more ancient a form is, the more often, apparently, it displays characters in some degree intermediate between groups now distinct; for the more ancient a form is, the more nearly it will be related to, and consequently resemble, the common progenitor of groups, since become widely divergent. Extinct forms are seldom directly intermediate between existing forms; but are intermediate only by a long and circuitous course through many extinct and very different forms. We can clearly see why the organic remains of closely consecutive formations are more closely allied to each other, than are those of remote formations; for the forms are more closely linked together by generation: we can clearly see why the remains of an intermediate formation are intermediate in character.

The inhabitants of each successive period in the world's history have beaten their predecessors in the race for life, and are, in so far, higher in the scale of nature; and this may account for that vague yet ill-defined sentiment, felt by many palaeontologists, that organisation on the whole has progressed. If it should hereafter be proved that ancient animals resemble to a certain extent the embryos of more recent animals of the same class, the fact will be intelligible. The succession of the same types of structure within the same areas during the later geological periods ceases to be mysterious, and is simply explained by inheritance.

If then the geological record be as imperfect as I believe it to be, and it may at least be asserted that the record cannot be proved to be much more perfect, the main objections to the theory of natural selection are greatly diminished or disappear. On the other hand, all the chief laws of palaeontology plainly proclaim, as it seems to me, that species have been produced by ordinary generation: old forms having been supplanted by new and improved forms of life, produced by the laws of variation still acting round us, and preserved by Natural Selection.

Geographical Distribution

In considering the distribution of organic beings over the face of the globe, the first great fact which strikes us is, that neither the similarity nor the dissimilarity of the inhabitants of various regions can be accounted for by their climatal and other physical conditions. Of late, almost every author who has studied the subject has come to this conclusion. The case of America alone would almost suffice to prove its truth: for if we exclude the northern parts where the circumpolar land is almost continuous, all authors agree that one of the most fundamental divisions in geographical distribution is that between the New and Old Worlds; yet if we travel over the vast American continent, from the central parts of the United States to its extreme southern point, we meet with the most diversified conditions; the most humid districts, arid deserts, lofty mountains, grassy plains, forests, marshes, lakes, and great rivers, under almost every temperature. There is hardly a climate or condition in the Old World which cannot be paralleled in the New – at least as closely as the same species generally require; for it is a most rare case to find a group of organisms confined to any small spot, having conditions peculiar in only a slight degree; for instance, small areas in the Old World could be pointed out hotter than any in the New World, yet these are not inhabited by a peculiar fauna or flora.

Notwithstanding this parallelism in the conditions of the Old and New Worlds, how widely different are their living productions!

In the southern hemisphere, if we compare large tracts of land in Australia, South Africa, and western South America, between latitudes 25° and 35°, we shall find parts extremely similar in all their conditions, yet it would not be possible to point out three faunas and floras more utterly dissimilar. Or again we may compare the productions of South America south of lat. 35° with those north of 25°, which consequently inhabit a considerably different climate, and they will be found incomparably more closely related to each other, than they are to the productions of Australia or Africa under nearly the same climate. Analogous facts could be given with respect to the inhabitants of the sea.

A second great fact which strikes us in our general review is, that barriers of any kind, or obstacles to free migration, are related in a close and important manner to the differences between the productions of various regions. We see this in the great difference of nearly all the terrestrial productions of the New and Old Worlds, excepting in the northern parts, where the land almost joins, and where, under a slightly different climate, there might have been free migration for the northern temperate forms, as there now is for the strictly arctic productions. We see the same fact in the great difference between the inhabitants of Australia, Africa, and South America under the same latitude: for these countries are almost as much isolated from each other as is possible. On each continent, also, we see the same fact; for on the opposite sides of lofty and continuous mountain-ranges, and of great deserts, and sometimes even of large rivers, we find different productions; though as mountain-chains, deserts, &c., are not as impassable, or likely to have endured so long as the oceans separating continents, the differences are very inferior in degree to those characteristic of distinct continents.

Turning to the sea, we find the same law. No two marine faunas are more distinct, with hardly a fish, shell, or crab in common, than those of the eastern and western shores of South and Central America; yet these great faunas are separated only by the narrow, but impassable, isthmus of Panama. Westward of the shores of America, a wide space of open ocean extends, with not an island as a halting-place for emigrants; here we have a barrier of another kind, and as soon as this is passed we meet in the eastern islands of the Pacific, with another and totally distinct fauna. So that here three marine faunas range far northward and southward, in parallel lines not far from each other, under corresponding climates; but from being separated from each other by impassable barriers, either of land or open sea, they are wholly distinct. On the other hand, proceeding still further westward from the eastern islands of the tropical parts of the Pacific, we encounter no impassable barriers, and we have innumerable islands as halting-places, until after travelling over a hemisphere we come to the shores of Africa; and over this vast space we meet with no well-defined and distinct marine faunas. Although hardly one shell, crab or fish is common to the above-named three approximate faunas of Eastern and Western America and the eastern Pacific islands, yet many fish range from the Pacific into the Indian Ocean, and many shells are common to the eastern islands of the Pacific and the eastern shores of Africa, on almost exactly opposite meridians of longitude.

A third great fact, partly included in the foregoing statements, is the affinity of the productions of the same continent or sea, though the species themselves are distinct at different points and stations. It is a law of the widest generality, and every continent offers innumerable instances. Nevertheless the naturalist in travelling, for instance, from north to south never fails to be struck by the manner in which successive groups of beings, specifically distinct, yet clearly related, replace each other. He hears from closely allied, yet distinct kinds of birds, notes nearly similar, and sees their nests similarly constructed, but not quite alike, with eggs coloured in nearly the same manner. The plains near the Straits of Magellan are inhabited by one species of Rhea (American ostrich), and northward the plains of La Plata by another species of the same genus; and not by a true ostrich or emeu, like those found in Africa and Australia under the same latitude. On these same plains of La Plata, we see the agouti and bizcacha, animals having nearly the same habits as our hares and rabbits and belonging to the same order of Rodents, but they plainly display an American type of structure. We ascend the lofty peaks of the Cordillera and we find an alpine species of bizcacha; we look to the waters, and we do not find the beaver or musk-rat, but the coypu and capybara, rodents of the American type. Innumerable other instances could be given. If we look to the islands off the American shore, however much they may differ in geological structure, the inhabitants, though they may be all peculiar species, are essentially American. We may look back to past ages, as shown in the last chapter, and we find American types then prevalent on the American continent and in the American seas. We see in these facts some deep organic bond, prevailing throughout space and time, over the same areas of land and water, and independent of their physical conditions. The naturalist must feel little curiosity, who is not led to inquire what this bond is.

This bond, on my theory, is simply inheritance, that cause which alone, as far as we positively know, produces organisms quite like, or, as we see in the case of varieties nearly like each other. The dissimilarity of the inhabitants of different regions may be attributed to modification through natural selection, and in a quite subordinate degree to the direct influence of different physical conditions. The degree of dissimilarity will depend on the migration of the more dominant forms of life from one region into another having been effected with more or less ease, at periods more or less remote; – on the nature and number of the former immigrants; – and on their action and reaction, in their mutual struggles for life; – the relation of organism to organism being, as I have already often remarked, the most important of all relations. Thus the high importance of barriers comes into play by checking migration; as does time for the slow process of modification through natural selection. Widely-ranging species, abounding in individuals, which have already triumphed over many competitors in their own widely-extended homes will have the best chance of seizing on new places, when they spread into new countries. In their new homes they will be exposed to new conditions, and will frequently undergo further modification and improvement; and thus they will become still further victorious, and will produce groups of modified descendants. On this principle of inheritance with modification, we can understand how it is that sections of genera, whole genera, and even families are confined to the same areas, as is so commonly and notoriously the case.

I believe, as was remarked in the last chapter, in no law of necessary development. As the variability of each species is an independent property, and will be taken advantage of by natural selection, only so far as it profits the individual in its complex struggle for life, so the degree of modification in different species will be no uniform quantity. If, for instance, a number of species, which stand in direct competition with each other, migrate in a body into a new and afterwards isolated country, they will be little liable to modification; for neither migration nor isolation in themselves can do anything. These principles come into play only by bringing organisms into new relations with each other, and in a lesser degree with the surrounding physical conditions. As we have seen in the last chapter that some forms have retained nearly the same character from an enormously remote geological period, so certain species have migrated over vast spaces, and have not become greatly modified.

On these views, it is obvious, that the several species of the same genus, though inhabiting the most distant quarters of the world, must originally have proceeded from the same source, as they have descended from the same progenitor. In the case of those species, which have undergone during whole geological periods but little modification, there is not much difficulty in believing that they may have migrated from the same region; for during the vast geographical and climatal changes which will have supervened since ancient times, almost any amount of migration is possible. But in many other cases, in which we have reason to believe that the species of a genus have been produced within comparatively recent times, there is great difficulty on this head. It is also obvious that the individuals of the same species, though now inhabiting distant and isolated regions, must have proceeded from one spot, where their parents were first produced: for, as explained in the last chapter, it is incredible that individuals identically the same should ever have been produced through natural selection from parents specifically distinct.

We are thus brought to the question which has been largely discussed by naturalists, namely, whether species have been created at one or more points of the earth's surface. Undoubtedly there are very many cases of extreme difficulty, in understanding how the same species could possibly have migrated from some one point to the several distant and isolated points, where now found. Nevertheless the simplicity of the view that each species was first produced within a single region captivates the mind. He who rejects it, rejects the *vera causa* of ordinary generation with subsequent migration, and calls in the agency of a miracle. It is universally admitted, that in most cases the area inhabited by a species is continuous; and when a plant or animal inhabits two points so distant from each other, or with an interval of such a nature, that the space could not be easily passed over by migration, the fact is given as something remarkable and exceptional. The capacity of migrating across the sea is more distinctly limited in terrestrial mammals, than perhaps in any other organic beings; and, accordingly, we find no inexplicable cases of the same mammal inhabiting distant points of the world. No geologist will feel any difficulty in such cases as Great Britain having been formerly united to Europe, and consequently possessing the same quadrupeds. But if the same species can be produced at two separate points, why do we not find a single mammal common to Europe and Australia or South America? The conditions of life are nearly the same, so that a multitude of European animals and plants have become naturalised in America and Australia; and some of the aboriginal plants are identically the same at these distant points of the northern and southern hemispheres? The answer, as I believe, is, that mammals have not been able to migrate, whereas some plants, from their varied means of dispersal, have migrated across the vast and broken inter-space. The great and striking influence which barriers of every kind have had on distribution, is intelligible only on the view that the great majority of species have been produced on one side alone, and have not been able to migrate to the other side. Some few families, many subfamilies, very many genera, and a still greater number of sections of genera are confined to a single region; and it has been observed by several naturalists, that the most natural genera, or those genera in which the species are most closely related to each other, are generally local, or confined to one area. What a strange anomaly it would be, if, when coming one step lower in the series, to the individuals of the same species, a directly opposite rule prevailed; and species were not local, but had been produced in two or more distinct areas!

Hence it seems to me, as it has to many other naturalists, that the view of each species having been produced in one area alone, and having subsequently migrated from that area as far as its powers of migration and subsistence under past and present conditions permitted, is the most probable. Undoubtedly many cases occur, in which we cannot explain how the same species could have passed from one point to the other. But the geographical and climatal changes, which have certainly occurred within recent geological times, must have interrupted or rendered discontinuous the formerly continuous range of many species. So that we are reduced to consider whether the exceptions to continuity of range are so numerous and of so grave a nature, that we ought to give up the belief, rendered probable by general considerations, that each species has been produced within one area, and has migrated thence as far as it could. It would be hopelessly tedious to discuss all the exceptional cases of the same species, now living at distant and separated points; nor do I for a moment pretend that any explanation could be offered of many such cases. But after some preliminary remarks, I will discuss a few of the most striking classes of facts; namely, the existence of the same species on the summits of distant mountain-ranges, and at distant points in the arctic and antarctic regions; and secondly (in the following chapter), the wide distribution of freshwater productions; and thirdly, the occurrence of the same terrestrial species on islands and on the mainland, though separated by hundreds of miles of open sea. If the existence of the same species at distant and isolated points of the earth's surface, can in many instances be explained on the view of each species having migrated from a single birthplace; then, considering our ignorance with respect to former climatal and geographical changes and various occasional means of transport, the belief that this has been the universal law, seems to me incomparably the safest.

In discussing this subject, we shall be enabled at the same time to consider a point equally important for us, namely, whether the several distinct species of a genus, which on my theory have all descended from a common progenitor, can have migrated (undergoing modification during some part of their migration) from the area inhabited by their progenitor. If it can be shown to be almost invariably the case, that a region, of which most of its inhabitants are closely related to, or belong to the same genera with the species of a second region, has probably received at some former period immigrants from this other region, my theory will be strengthened; for we can clearly understand, on the principle of modification, why the inhabitants of a region should be related to those of another region, whence it has been stocked. A volcanic island, for instance, upheaved and formed at the distance of a few hundreds of miles from a continent, would probably receive from it in the course of time a few colonists, and their descendants, though modified, would still be plainly related by inheritance to the inhabitants of the continent. Cases of this nature are common, and are, as we shall hereafter more fully see, inexplicable on the theory of independent creation. This view of the relation of species in one region to those in another, does not differ much (by substituting the word variety for species) from that lately advanced in an ingenious paper by Mr Wallace, in which he concludes, that 'every species has come into existence coincident both in space and time with a pre-existing closely allied species'. And I now know from correspondence, that this coincidence he attributes to generation with modification.

The previous remarks on 'single and multiple centres of creation' do not directly bear on another allied question – namely whether all the individuals of the same species have descended from a single pair, or single hermaphrodite, or whether, as some authors suppose, from many individuals simultaneously created. With those organic beings which never intercross (if such exist), the species, on my theory, must have descended from a succession of improved varieties, which will never have blended with other individuals or varieties, but will have supplanted each other; so that, at each successive stage of modification and improvement, all the individuals of each variety will have descended from a single parent. But in the majority of cases, namely, with all organisms which habitually unite for each birth, or which often intercross, I believe that during the slow process of modification the individuals of the species will have been kept nearly uniform by intercrossing; so that many individuals will have gone on simultaneously changing, and the whole amount of modification will not have been due, at each stage, to descent from a single parent. To illustrate what I mean: our English race-horses differ slightly from the horses of every other breed; but they do not owe their difference and superiority to descent from any single pair, but to continued care in selecting and training many individuals during many generations.

Before discussing the three classes of facts, which I have selected as presenting the greatest amount of difficulty on the theory of 'single centres of creation', I must say a few words on the means of dispersal.

Means of Dispersal – Sir C. Lyell and other authors have ably treated this subject. I can give here only the briefest abstract of the more important facts. Change of climate must have had a powerful influence on migration: a region when its climate was different may have been a high road for migration, but now be impassable; I shall, however, presently have to discuss this branch of the subject in some detail. Changes of level in the land must also have been highly influential: a narrow isthmus now separates two marine faunas; submerge it, or let it formerly have been submerged, and the two faunas will now blend or may formerly have blended: where the sea now extends, land may at a former period have connected islands or possibly even continents together, and thus have allowed terrestrial productions to pass from one to the other. No geologist will dispute that great mutations of level, have occurred within the period of existing organisms. Edward Forbes insisted that all the islands in the Atlantic must recently have been connected with Europe or Africa, and Europe likewise with America. Other authors have thus hypothetically bridged over every ocean, and have united almost every island to some mainland. If indeed the arguments used by Forbes are to be trusted, it must be admitted that scarcely a single island exists which has not recently been united to some continent. This view cuts the Gordian knot of the dispersal of the same species to the most distant points, and removes many a difficulty: but to the best of my judgment we are not authorized in admitting such enormous geographical changes within the period of existing species. It seems to me that we have abundant evidence of great oscillations of level in our continents; but not of such vast changes in their position and extension, as to have united them within the recent period to each other and to the several intervening oceanic islands. I freely admit the former existence of many islands, now buried beneath the sea, which may have served as halting places for plants and for many animals during their migration. In the coral-producing oceans such sunken islands are now marked, as I believe, by rings of coral or atolls standing over them. Whenever it is fully admitted, as I believe it will some day be, that each species has proceeded from a single birthplace, and when in the course of time we know something definite about the means of distribution, we shall be enabled to speculate with security on the former extension of the land. But I do not believe that it will ever be proved that within the recent period continents which are now quite separate, have been continuously, or almost continuously, united with each other, and with the many existing oceanic islands. Several facts in distribution – such as the great difference in the marine faunas on the opposite sides of almost every continent – the close relation of the tertiary inhabitants of several lands and even seas to their present inhabitants – a certain degree of relation (as we shall hereafter see) between the distribution of mammals and the depth of the sea – these and other such facts seem to me opposed to the admission of such prodigious geographical revolutions within the recent period, as are necessitated on the view advanced by Forbes and admitted by his many followers. The nature and relative proportions of the inhabitants of oceanic islands likewise seem to me opposed to the belief of their former continuity with continents. Nor does their almost universally volcanic composition favour the admission that they are the wrecks of sunken continents; – if they had originally existed as mountain-ranges on the land, some at least of the islands would have been formed, like other mountain-summits, of granite, metamorphic schists, old fossiliferous or other such rocks, instead of consisting of mere piles of volcanic matter.

I must now say a few words on what are called accidental means, but which more properly might be called occasional means of distribution. I shall here confine myself to plants. In botanical works, this or that plant is stated to be ill adapted for wide dissemination; but for transport across the sea, the greater or less facilities may be said to be almost wholly unknown. Until I tried, with Mr Berkeley's aid, a few experiments, it was not even known how far seeds could resist the injurious action of sea-water. To my surprise I found that out of 87 kinds, 64 germinated after an immersion of 28 days, and a few survived an immersion of 137 days. For convenience sake

I chiefly tried small seeds, without the capsule or fruit; and as all of these sank in a few days, they could not be floated across wide spaces of the sea, whether or not they were injured by the salt-water. Afterwards I tried some larger fruits, capsules, &c., and some of these floated for a long time. It is well known what a difference there is in the buoyancy of green and seasoned timber; and it occurred to me that floods might wash down plants or branches, and that these might be dried on the banks, and then by a fresh rise in the stream be washed into the sea. Hence I was led to dry stems and branches of 94 plants with ripe fruit, and to place them on sea-water. The majority sank quickly, but some which whilst green floated for a very short time, when dried floated much longer; for instance, ripe hazel-nuts sank immediately, but when dried, they floated for 90 days and afterwards when planted they germinated; an asparagus plant with ripe berries floated for 23 days, when dried it floated for 85 days, and the seeds afterwards germinated: the ripe seeds of Helosciadium sank in two days, when dried they floated for above 90 days, and afterwards germinated. Altogether out of the 94 dried plants, 18 floated for above 28 days, and some of the 18 floated for a very much longer period. So that as 64/87 seeds germinated after an immersion of 28 days; and as 18/94 plants with ripe fruit (but not all the same species as in the foregoing experiment) floated, after being dried, for above 28 days, as far as we may infer anything from these scanty facts, we may conclude that the seeds of 14/100 plants of any country might be floated by sea-currents during 28 days, and would retain their power of germination. In Johnston's

Physical Atlas, the average rate of the several Atlantic currents is 33 miles per diem (some currents running at the rate of 60 miles per diem); on this average, the seeds of 14/100 plants belonging to one country might be floated across 924 miles of sea to another country; and when stranded, if blown to a favourable spot by an inland gale, they would germinate.

Subsequently to my experiments, M. Martens tried similar ones, but in a much better manner, for he placed the seeds in a box in the actual sea, so that they were alternately wet and exposed to the air like really floating plants. He tried 98 seeds, mostly different from mine; but he chose many large fruits and likewise seeds from plants which live near the sea; and this would have favoured the average length of their flotation and of their resistance to the injurious action of the salt-water. On the other hand he did not previously dry the plants or branches with the fruit; and this, as we have seen, would have caused some of them to have floated much longer. The result was that 18/98 of his seeds floated for 42 days, and were then capable of germination. But I do not doubt that plants exposed to the waves would float for a less time than those protected from violent movement as in our experiments. Therefore it would perhaps be safer to assume that the seeds of about 10/100 plants of a flora, after having been dried, could be floated across a space of sea 900 miles in width, and would then germinate. The fact of the larger fruits often floating longer than the small, is interesting; as plants with large seeds or fruit could hardly be transported by any other means; and Alph. de Candolle has shown that such plants generally have restricted ranges.

But seeds may be occasionally transported in another manner. Drift timber is thrown up on most islands, even on those in the midst of the widest oceans; and the natives of the coral-islands in the Pacific, procure stones for their tools, solely from the roots of drifted trees, these stones being a valuable royal tax. I find on examination, that when irregularly shaped stones are embedded in the roots of trees, small parcels of earth are very frequently enclosed in their interstices and behind them – so perfectly that not a particle could be washed away in the longest transport: out of one small portion of earth thus *completely* enclosed by wood in an oak about 50 years old, three dicotyledonous plants germinated: I am certain of the accuracy of this observation. Again, I can show that the carcasses of birds, when floating on the sea, sometimes escape being immediately devoured; and seeds of many kinds in the crops of floating birds long retain their vitality: peas and vetches, for instance, are killed by even a few days' immersion in sea-water; but some taken out of the crop of a pigeon, which had floated on artificial salt-water for 30 days, to my surprise nearly all germinated.

Living birds can hardly fail to be highly effective agents in the transportation of seeds. I could give many facts showing how frequently birds of many kinds are blown by gales to vast distances across the ocean. We may I think safely assume that under such circumstances their rate of flight would often be 35 miles an hour; and some authors have given a far higher estimate. I have never seen an instance of nutritious seeds passing through the intestines of a bird; but hard seeds of fruit will pass uninjured through even the digestive organs of a turkey.

In the course of two months, I picked up in my garden 12 kinds of seeds, out of the excrement of small birds, and these seemed perfect, and some of them, which I tried, germinated. But the following fact is more important: the crops of birds do not secrete gastric juice, and do not in the least injure, as I know by trial, the germination of seeds; now after a bird has found and devoured a large supply of food, it is positively asserted that all the grains do not pass into the gizzard for 12 or even 18 hours. A bird in this interval might easily be blown to the distance of 500 miles, and hawks are known to look out for tired birds, and the contents of their torn crops might thus readily get scattered. Mr Brent informs me that a friend of his had to give up flying carrier-pigeons from France to England, as the hawks on the English coast destroyed so many on their arrival. Some hawks and owls bolt their prey whole, and after an interval of from twelve to twenty hours, disgorge pellets, which, as I know from experiments made in the Zoological Gardens, include seeds capable of germination. Some seeds of the oat, wheat, millet, canary, hemp, clover, and beet germinated after having been from twelve to twenty-one hours in the stomachs of different birds of prey; and two seeds of beet grew after having been thus retained for two days and fourteen hours. Fresh-water fish, I find, eat seeds of many land and water plants: fish are frequently devoured by birds, and thus the seeds might be transported from place to place. I forced many kinds of seeds into the stomachs of dead fish, and then gave their bodies to fishing-eagles, storks, and pelicans; these birds after an interval of many hours, either rejected the seeds in pellets or passed them in their excrement; and several of these seeds retained their power of germination. Certain seeds, however, were always killed by this process.

Although the beaks and feet of birds are generally quite clean, I can show that earth sometimes adheres to them: in one instance I removed twenty-two grains of dry argillaceous earth from one foot of a partridge, and in this earth there was a pebble quite as large as the seed of a vetch. Thus seeds might occasionally be transported to great distances; for many facts could be given showing that soil almost everywhere is charged with seeds. Reflect for a moment on the millions of quails which annually cross the Mediterranean; and can we doubt that the earth adhering to their feet would sometimes include a few minute seeds? But I shall presently have to recur to this subject.

As icebergs are known to be sometimes loaded with earth and stones, and have even carried brushwood, bones, and the nest of a land-bird, I can hardly doubt that they must occasionally have transported seeds from one part to another of the arctic and antarctic regions, as suggested by Lyell; and during the Glacial period from one part of the now temperate regions to another. In the Azores, from the large number of the species of plants common to Europe, in comparison with the plants of other oceanic islands nearer to the mainland, and (as remarked by Mr H. C. Watson) from the somewhat northern character of the flora in comparison with the latitude, I suspected that these islands had been partly stocked by ice-borne seeds, during the Glacial epoch. At my request Sir C. Lyell wrote to M. Hartung to inquire whether he had observed erratic boulders on these islands, and he answered that he had found large fragments of granite and other rocks, which do not occur in the archipelago. Hence we may safely infer that icebergs formerly landed their rocky burthens on the shores of these mid-ocean islands, and it is at least possible that they may have brought thither the seeds of northern plants.

Considering that the several above means of transport, and that several other means, which without doubt remain to be discovered, have been in action year after year, for centuries and tens of thousands of years, it would I think be a marvellous fact if many plants had not thus become widely transported. These means of transport are sometimes called accidental, but this is not strictly correct: the currents of the sea are not accidental, nor is the direction of prevalent gales of wind. It should be observed that scarcely any means of transport would carry seeds for very great distances; for seeds do not retain their vitality when exposed for a great length of time to the action of sea-water; nor could they be long carried in the crops or intestines of birds. These means, however, would suffice for occasional transport across tracts of sea some hundred miles in breadth, or from island to island, or from a continent to a neighbouring island, but not from one distant continent to another. The floras of distant continents would not by such means become mingled in any great degree; but would remain as distinct as we now see them to be. The currents, from their course, would never bring seeds from North America to Britain, though they might and do bring seeds from the West Indies to our western shores, where, if not killed by so long an immersion in salt-water, they could not endure our climate. Almost every year, one or two land-birds are blown across the whole Atlantic Ocean, from North America to the western shores of Ireland and England; but seeds could be transported by these wanderers only by one means, namely, in dirt sticking to their feet, which is in itself a rare accident. Even in this case, how small would the chance be of a seed falling on favourable soil, and coming to maturity! But it would be a great error to argue that because a well-stocked island, like Great Britain, has not, as far as is known (and it would be very difficult to prove this), received within the last few centuries, through occasional means of transport, immigrants from Europe or any other continent, that a poorly-stocked island, though standing more remote from the mainland, would not receive colonists by similar means. I do not doubt that out of twenty seeds or animals transported to an island, even if far less well-stocked than Britain, scarcely more than one would be so well fitted to its new home, as to become naturalised. But this, as it seems to me, is no valid argument against what would be effected by occasional means of transport, during the long lapse of geological time, whilst an island was being upheaved and formed, and before it had become fully stocked with inhabitants. On almost bare land, with few or no destructive insects or birds living there, nearly every seed, which chanced to arrive, would be sure to germinate and survive.

Dispersal during the Glacial period – The identity of many plants and animals, on mountain-summits, separated from each other by hundreds of miles of lowlands, where the Alpine species could not possibly exist, is one of the most striking cases known of the same species living at distant points, without the apparent possibility of their having migrated from one to the other. It is indeed a remarkable fact to see so many of the same plants living on the snowy regions of the Alps or Pyrenees, and in the extreme northern parts of Europe; but it is far more remarkable, that the plants on the White Mountains, in the United States of America, are all the same with those of Labrador, and nearly all the same, as we hear from Asa Gray, with those on the loftiest mountains of Europe. Even as long ago as 1747, such facts led Gmelin to conclude that the same species must have been independently created at several distinct points; and we might have remained in this same belief, had not Agassiz and others called vivid attention to the Glacial period, which, as we shall immediately see, affords a simple explanation of these facts. We have evidence of almost every conceivable kind, organic and inorganic, that within a very recent geological period, central Europe and North America suffered under an Arctic climate. The ruins of a house burnt by fire do not tell their tale more plainly, than do the mountains of Scotland and Wales, with their scored flanks, polished surfaces, and perched boulders, of the icy streams with which their valleys were lately filled. So greatly has the climate of Europe changed, that in Northern Italy, gigantic moraines, left by old glaciers, are now clothed by the vine and maize. Throughout a large part of the United States, erratic boulders, and rocks scored by drifted icebergs and coast-ice, plainly reveal a former cold period.

The former influence of the glacial climate on the distribution of the inhabitants of Europe, as explained with remarkable clearness by Edward Forbes, is substantially as follows. But we shall follow the changes more readily, by supposing a new Glacial period to come slowly on, and then pass away, as formerly occurred. As the cold came on, and as each more southern zone became fitted for arctic beings and ill-fitted for their former more temperate inhabitants, the latter would be supplanted and arctic productions would take their places. The inhabitants of the more temperate regions would at the same time travel southward, unless they were stopped by barriers, in which case they would perish. The mountains would become covered with snow and ice, and their former Alpine inhabitants would descend to the plains. By the time that the cold had reached its maximum, we should have a uniform arctic fauna and flora, covering the central parts of Europe, as far south as the Alps and Pyrenees, and even stretching into Spain. The now temperate regions of the United States would likewise be covered by arctic plants and animals, and these would be nearly the same with those of Europe; for the present circumpolar inhabitants, which we suppose to have everywhere travelled southward, are remarkably uniform round the world. We may suppose that the Glacial period came on a little earlier or later in North America than in Europe, so will the southern migration there have been a little earlier or later; but this will make no difference in the final result.

As the warmth returned, the arctic forms would retreat northward, closely followed up in their retreat by the productions of the more temperate regions. And as the snow melted from the bases of the mountains, the arctic forms would seize on the cleared and thawed ground, always ascending higher and higher, as the warmth increased, whilst their brethren were pursuing their northern journey. Hence, when the warmth had fully returned, the same arctic species, which had lately lived in a body together on the lowlands of the Old and New Worlds, would be left isolated on distant mountain-summits (having been exterminated on all lesser heights) and in the arctic regions of both hemispheres.

Thus we can understand the identity of many plants at points so immensely remote as on the mountains of the United States and of Europe. We can thus also understand the fact that the Alpine plants of each mountain-range are more especially related to the arctic forms living due north or nearly due north of them: for the migration as the cold came on, and the re-migration on the returning warmth, will generally have been due south and north. The Alpine plants, for example, of Scotland, as remarked by Mr H. C. Watson, and those of the Pyrenees, as remarked by Ramond, are more especially allied to the plants of northern Scandinavia; those of the United States to Labrador; those of the mountains of Siberia to the arctic regions of that country. These views, grounded as they are on the perfectly well-ascertained occurrence of a former Glacial period, seem to me to explain in so satisfactory a manner the present distribution of the Alpine and Arctic productions of Europe and America, that when in other regions we find the same species on distant mountain-summits, we may almost conclude without other evidence, that a colder climate permitted their former migration across the low intervening tracts, since become too warm for their existence.

If the climate, since the Glacial period, has ever been in any degree warmer than at present (as some geologists in the United States believe to have been the case, chiefly from the distribution of the fossil Gnathodon), then the arctic and temperate productions will at a very late period have marched a little further north, and subsequently have retreated to their present homes; but I have met with no satisfactory evidence with respect to this intercalated slightly warmer period, since the Glacial period.

The arctic forms, during their long southern migration and re-migration northward, will have been exposed to nearly the same climate, and, as is especially to be noticed, they will have kept in a body together; consequently their mutual relations will not have been much disturbed, and, in accordance with the principles inculcated in this volume, they will not have been liable to much modification. But with our Alpine productions, left isolated from the moment of the returning warmth, first at the bases and ultimately on the summits of the mountains, the case will have been somewhat different; for it is not likely that all the same arctic species will have been left on mountain ranges distant from each other, and have survived there ever since; they will, also, in all probability have become mingled with ancient Alpine species, which must have existed on the mountains before the commencement of the Glacial epoch, and which during its coldest period will have been temporarily driven down to the plains; they will, also, have been exposed to somewhat different climatal influences. Their mutual relations will thus have been in some degree disturbed; consequently they will have been liable to modification; and this we find has been the case; for if we compare the present Alpine plants and animals of the several great European mountain-ranges, though very many of the species are identically the same, some present varieties, some are ranked as doubtful forms, and some few are distinct yet closely allied or representative species.

In illustrating what, as I believe, actually took place during the Glacial period, I assumed that at its commencement the arctic productions were as uniform round the polar regions as they are at the present day. But the foregoing remarks on distribution apply not only to strictly arctic forms, but also to many sub-arctic and to some few northern temperate forms, for some of these are the same on the lower mountains and on the plains of North America and Europe; and it may be reasonably asked how I account for the necessary degree of uniformity of the sub-arctic and northern temperate forms round the world, at the commencement of the Glacial period. At the present day, the sub-arctic and northern temperate productions of the Old and New Worlds are separated from each other by the Atlantic Ocean and by the extreme northern part of the Pacific. During the Glacial period, when the inhabitants of the Old and New Worlds lived further southwards than at present, they must have been still more completely separated by wider spaces of ocean. I believe the above difficulty may be surmounted by looking to still earlier changes of climate of an opposite nature. We have good reason to believe that during the newer

Pliocene period, before the Glacial epoch, and whilst the majority of the inhabitants of the world were specifically the same as now, the climate was warmer than at the present day. Hence we may suppose that the organisms now living under the climate of latitude 60°, during the Pliocene period lived further north under the Polar Circle, in latitude 66°–67°; and that the strictly arctic productions then lived on the broken land still nearer to the pole. Now if we look at a globe, we shall see that under the Polar Circle there is almost continuous land from western Europe, through Siberia, to eastern America. And to this continuity of the circumpolar land, and to the consequent freedom for intermigration under a more favourable climate, I attribute the necessary amount of uniformity in the sub-arctic and northern temperate productions of the Old and New Worlds, at a period anterior to the Glacial epoch.

Believing, from reasons before alluded to, that our continents have long remained in nearly the same relative position, though subjected to large, but partial oscillations of level, I am strongly inclined to extend the above view, and to infer that during some earlier and still warmer period, such as the older Pliocene period, a large number of the same plants and animals inhabited the almost continuous circumpolar land; and that these plants and animals, both in the Old and New Worlds, began slowly to migrate southwards as the climate became less warm, long before the commencement of the Glacial period. We now see, as I believe, their descendants, mostly in a modified condition, in the central parts of Europe and the United States. On this view we can understand the relationship, with very little identity, between the productions of North America and Europe – a relationship which is most remarkable, considering the distance of the two areas, and their separation by the Atlantic Ocean. We can further understand the singular fact remarked on by several observers, that the productions of Europe and America during the later tertiary stages were more closely related to each other than they are at the present time; for during these warmer periods the northern parts of the Old and New Worlds will have been almost continuously united by land, serving as a bridge, since rendered impassable by cold, for the inter-migration of their inhabitants.

During the slowly decreasing warmth of the Pliocene period, as soon as the species in common, which inhabited the New and Old Worlds, migrated south of the Polar Circle, they must have been completely cut off from each other. This separation, as far as the more temperate productions are concerned, took place long ages ago. And as the plants and animals migrated southward, they will have become mingled in the one great region with the native American productions, and have had to compete with them; and in the other great region, with those of the Old World. Consequently we have here everything favourable for much modification – for far more modification than with the Alpine productions, left isolated, within a much more recent period, on the several mountain-ranges and on the arctic lands of the two Worlds. Hence it has come, that when we compare the now living productions of the temperate regions of the New and Old Worlds, we find very few identical species (though Asa Gray has lately shown that more plants are identical than was formerly supposed), but we find in every great class many forms, which some naturalists rank as geographical races, and others as distinct species; and a host of closely allied or representative forms which are ranked by all naturalists as specifically distinct.

As on the land, so in the waters of the sea, a slow southern migration of a marine fauna, which during the Pliocene or even a somewhat earlier period, was nearly uniform along the continuous shores of the Polar Circle, will account, on the theory of modification, for many closely allied forms now living in areas completely sundered. Thus, I think, we can understand the presence of many existing and tertiary representative forms on the eastern and western shores of temperate North America; and the still more striking case of many closely allied crustaceans (as described in Dana's admirable work), of some fish and other marine animals, in the Mediterranean and in the seas of Japan – areas now separated by a continent and by nearly a hemisphere of equatorial ocean.

These cases of relationship, without identity, of the inhabitants of seas now disjoined, and likewise of the past and present inhabitants of the temperate lands of North America and Europe, are inexplicable on the theory of creation. We cannot say that they have been created alike, in correspondence with the nearly similar physical conditions of the areas; for if we compare, for instance, certain parts of South America with the southern continents of the Old World, we see countries closely corresponding in all their physical conditions, but with their inhabitants utterly dissimilar.

But we must return to our more immediate subject, the Glacial period. I am convinced that Forbes's view may be largely extended. In Europe we have the plainest evidence of the cold period, from the western shores of Britain to the Oural range, and southward to the Pyrenees. We may infer, from the frozen mammals and nature of the mountain vegetation, that Siberia was similarly affected. Along the Himalaya, at points 900 miles apart, glaciers have left the marks of their former low descent; and in Sikkim, Dr Hooker saw maize growing on gigantic ancient moraines. South of the equator, we have some direct evidence of former glacial action in New Zealand; and the same plants, found on widely separated mountains in this island, tell the same story. If one account which has been published can be trusted, we have direct evidence of glacial action in the south-eastern corner of Australia.

Looking to America; in the northern half, ice-borne fragments of rock have been observed on the eastern side as far south as lat. 36°–37°, and on the shores of the Pacific, where the climate is now so different, as far south as lat. 46°; erratic boulders have, also, been noticed on the Rocky Mountains. In the Cordillera of Equatorial South America, glaciers once extended far below their present level. In central Chile I was astonished at the structure of a vast mound of detritus, about 800 feet in height, crossing a valley of the Andes; and this I now feel convinced was a gigantic moraine, left far below any existing glacier. Further south on both sides of the continent, from lat. 41° to the southernmost extremity, we have the clearest evidence of former glacial action, in huge boulders transported far from their parent source.

We do not know that the Glacial epoch was strictly simultaneous at these several far distant points on opposite sides of the world. But we have good evidence in almost every case, that the epoch was included within the latest geological period. We have, also, excellent evidence, that it endured for an enormous time, as measured by years, at each point. The cold may have come on, or have ceased, earlier at one point of the globe than at another, but seeing that it endured for long at each, and that it was contemporaneous in a geological sense, it seems to me probable that it was, during a part at least of the period, actually simultaneous throughout the world. Without some distinct evidence to the contrary, we may at least admit as probable that the glacial action was simultaneous on the eastern and western sides of North America, in the Cordillera under the equator and under the warmer temperate zones, and on both sides of the southern extremity of the continent. If this be admitted, it is difficult to avoid believing that the temperature of the whole world was at this period simultaneously cooler. But it would suffice for my purpose, if the temperature was at the same time lower along certain broad belts of longitude.

On this view of the whole world, or at least of broad longitudinal belts, having been simultaneously colder from pole to pole, much light can be thrown on the present distribution of identical and allied species. In America, Dr Hooker has shown that between forty and fifty of the flowering plants of Tierra del Fuego, forming no inconsiderable part of its scanty flora, are common to Europe, enormously remote as these two points are; and there are many closely allied species. On the lofty mountains of equatorial America a host of peculiar species belonging to European genera occur. On the highest mountains of Brazil, some few European genera were found by Gardner, which do not exist in the wide intervening hot countries. So on the Silla of Caraccas the illustrious Humboldt long ago found species belonging to genera characteristic of the Cordillera. On the mountains of Abyssinia, several European forms and some few representatives of the peculiar flora of the Cape of Good Hope occur. At the Cape of Good Hope a very few European species, believed not to have been introduced by man, and on the mountains, some few representative European forms are found, which have not been discovered in the intertropical parts of Africa. On the Himalaya, and on the isolated mountain-ranges of the peninsula of India, on the heights of Ceylon, and on the volcanic cones of Java, many plants occur, either identically the same or representing each other, and at the same time representing plants of Europe, not found in the intervening hot lowlands. A list of the genera collected on the loftier peaks of Java raises a picture of a collection made on a hill in Europe! Still more striking is the fact that southern Australian forms are clearly represented by plants growing on the summits of the mountains of Borneo. Some of these Australian forms, as I hear from Dr Hooker, extend along the heights of the peninsula of Malacca, and are thinly scattered, on the one hand over India and on the other as far north as Japan.

On the southern mountains of Australia, Dr F. Müller has discovered several European species; other species, not introduced by man, occur on the lowlands; and a long list can be given, as I am informed by Dr Hooker, of

European genera, found in Australia, but not in the intermediate torrid regions. In the admirable 'Introduction to the Flora of New Zealand', by Dr Hooker, analogous and striking facts are given in regard to the plants of that large island. Hence we see that throughout the world, the plants growing on the more lofty mountains, and on the temperate lowlands of the northern and southern hemispheres, are sometimes identically the same; but they are much oftener specifically distinct, though related to each other in a most remarkable manner.

This brief abstract applies to plants alone: some strictly analogous facts could be given on the distribution of terrestrial animals. In marine productions, similar cases occur; as an example, I may quote a remark by the highest authority, Prof. Dana, that 'it is certainly a wonderful fact that New Zealand should have a closer resemblance in its crustacea to Great Britain, its antipode, than to any other part of the world'. Sir J. Richardson, also, speaks of the reappearance on the shores of New Zealand, Tasmania, &c., of northern forms of fish. Dr Hooker informs me that twenty-five species of Algae are common to New Zealand and to Europe, but have not been found in the intermediate tropical seas.

It should be observed that the northern species and forms found in the southern parts of the southern hemisphere, and on the mountain-ranges of the intertropical regions, are not arctic, but belong to the northern temperate zones. As Mr H. C. Watson has recently remarked, 'In receding from polar towards equatorial latitudes, the Alpine or mountain floras really become less and less arctic.' Many of the forms living on the mountains of the warmer regions of the earth and in the southern hemisphere are of doubtful value, being ranked by some naturalists as specifically distinct, by others as varieties; but some are certainly identical, and many, though closely related to northern forms, must be ranked as distinct species.

Now let us see what light can be thrown on the foregoing facts, on the belief, supported as it is by a large body of geological evidence, that the whole world, or a large part of it, was during the Glacial period simultaneously much colder than at present. The Glacial period, as measured by years, must have been very long; and when we remember over what vast spaces some naturalised plants and animals have spread within a few centuries, this period will have been ample for any amount of migration. As the cold came slowly on, all the tropical plants and other productions will have retreated from both sides towards the equator, followed in the rear by the temperate productions, and these by the arctic; but with the latter we are not now concerned. The tropical plants probably suffered much extinction; how much no one can say; perhaps formerly the tropics supported as many species as we see at the present day crowded together at the Cape of Good Hope, and in parts of temperate Australia. As we know that many tropical plants and animals can withstand a considerable amount of cold, many might have escaped extermination during a moderate fall of temperature, more especially by escaping into the warmest spots. But the great fact to bear in mind is, that all tropical productions will have suffered to a certain extent. On the other hand, the temperate productions, after migrating nearer to the equator, though they will have been placed under somewhat new conditions, will have suffered less. And it is certain that many temperate plants, if protected from the inroads of competitors, can withstand a much warmer climate than their own. Hence, it seems to me possible, bearing in mind that the tropical productions were in a suffering state and could not have presented a firm front against intruders, that a certain number of the more vigorous and dominant temperate forms might have penetrated the native ranks and have reached or even crossed the equator. The invasion would, of course, have been greatly favoured by high land, and perhaps by a dry climate; for Dr Falconer informs me that it is the damp with the heat of the tropics which is so destructive to perennial plants from a temperate climate. On the other hand, the most humid and hottest districts will have afforded an asylum to the tropical natives. The mountain-ranges north-west of the Himalaya, and the long line of the Cordillera, seem to have afforded two great lines of invasion: and it is a striking fact, lately communicated to me by Dr Hooker, that all the flowering plants, about forty-six in number, common to Tierra del Fuego and to Europe still exist in North America, which must have lain on the line of march. But I do not doubt that some temperate productions entered and crossed even the *lowlands* of the tropics at the period when the cold was most intense – when arctic forms had migrated some twenty-five degrees of latitude from their native country and covered the land at the foot of the Pyrenees. At this period of extreme cold, I believe that the climate under the equator at the level of the sea was about the same with that now felt there at the height of six or seven thousand feet. During this the coldest period, I suppose that large spaces of the tropical lowlands were clothed with a mingled tropical and temperate vegetation, like that now growing with strange luxuriance at the base of the Himalaya, as graphically described by Hooker.

Thus, as I believe, a considerable number of plants, a few terrestrial animals, and some marine productions, migrated during the Glacial period from the northern and southern temperate zones into the intertropical regions, and some even crossed the equator. As the warmth returned, these temperate forms would naturally ascend the higher mountains, being exterminated on the lowlands; those which had not reached the equator, would re-migrate northward or southward towards their former homes; but the forms, chiefly northern, which had crossed the equator, would travel still further from their homes into the more temperate latitudes of the opposite hemisphere. Although we have reason to believe from geological evidence that the whole body of arctic shells underwent scarcely any modification during their long southern migration and re-migration northward, the case may have been wholly different with those intruding forms which settled themselves on the intertropical mountains, and in the southern hemisphere. These being surrounded by strangers will have had to compete with many new forms of life; and it is probable that selected modifications in their structure, habits, and constitutions will have profited them. Thus many of these wanderers, though still plainly related by inheritance to their brethren of the northern or southern hemispheres, now exist in their new homes as well-marked varieties or as distinct species.

It is a remarkable fact, strongly insisted on by Hooker in regard to America, and by Alph. de Candolle in regard to Australia, that many more identical plants and allied forms have apparently migrated from the north to the south, than in a reversed direction. We see, however, a few southern vegetable forms on the mountains of Borneo and Abyssinia. I suspect that this preponderant migration from north to south is due to the greater extent of land in the north, and to the northern forms having existed in their own homes in greater numbers, and having consequently been advanced through natural selection and competition to a higher stage of perfection or dominating power, than the southern forms. And thus, when they became commingled during the Glacial period, the northern forms were enabled to beat the less powerful southern forms. Just in the same manner as we see at the present day, that very many European productions cover the ground in La Plata, and in a lesser degree in Australia, and have to a certain extent beaten the natives; whereas extremely few southern forms have become naturalised in any part of Europe, though hides, wool, and other objects likely to carry seeds have been largely imported into Europe during the last two or three centuries from La Plata, and during the last thirty or forty years from Australia. Something of the same kind must have occurred on the intertropical mountains: no doubt before the Glacial period they were stocked with endemic Alpine forms; but these have almost everywhere largely yielded to the more dominant forms, generated in the larger areas and more efficient workshops of the north. In many islands the native productions are nearly equalled or even outnumbered by the naturalised; and if the natives have not been actually exterminated, their numbers have been greatly reduced, and this is the first stage towards extinction. A mountain is an island on the land; and the intertropical mountains before the Glacial period must have been completely isolated; and I believe that the productions of these islands on the land yielded to those produced within the larger areas of the north, just in the same way as the productions of real islands have everywhere lately yielded to continental forms, naturalised by man's agency.

I am far from supposing that all difficulties are removed on the view here given in regard to the range and affinities of the allied species which live in the northern and southern temperate zones and on the mountains of the intertropical regions. Very many difficulties remain to be solved. I do not pretend to indicate the exact lines and means of migration, or the reason why certain species and not others have migrated; why certain species have been modified and have given rise to new groups of forms, and others have remained unaltered. We cannot hope to explain such facts, until we can say why one species and not another becomes naturalised by man's agency in a foreign land; why one ranges twice or thrice as far, and is twice or thrice as common, as another species within their own homes.

I have said that many difficulties remain to be solved: some of the most remarkable are stated with admirable clearness by Dr Hooker in his botanical works on the antarctic regions. These cannot be here discussed. I will only say that as far as regards the occurrence of identical species at points so enormously remote as Kerguelen Land, New Zealand, and Fuegia, I believe that towards the close of the Glacial period, icebergs, as suggested by Lyell, have been largely concerned in their dispersal. But the existence of several quite distinct species, belonging to genera exclusively confined to the south, at these and other distant points of the southern hemisphere, is, on my theory of descent with modification, a far more remarkable case of difficulty. For some of these species are so distinct, that we cannot suppose that there has been time since the commencement of the Glacial period for their migration, and for their subsequent modification to the necessary degree. The facts seem to me to indicate that peculiar and very distinct species have migrated in radiating lines from some common centre; and I am inclined to look in the southern, as in the northern hemisphere, to a former and warmer period, before the commencement of the Glacial period, when the antarctic lands, now covered with ice, supported a highly peculiar and isolated flora. I suspect that before this flora was exterminated by the Glacial epoch, a few forms were widely dispersed to various points of the southern hemisphere by occasional means of transport, and by the aid, as halting-places, of existing and now sunken islands, and perhaps at the commencement of the Glacial period, by icebergs. By these means, as I believe, the southern shores of America, Australia, New Zealand have become slightly tinted by the same peculiar forms of vegetable life.

Sir C. Lyell in a striking passage has speculated, in language almost identical with mine, on the effects of great alternations of climate on geographical distribution. I believe that the world has recently felt one of his great cycles of change; and that on this view, combined with modification through natural selection, a multitude of facts in the present distribution both of the same and of allied forms of life can be explained. The living waters may be said to have flowed during one short period from the north and from the south, and to have crossed at the equator; but to have flowed with greater force from the north so as to have freely inundated the south. As the tide leaves its drift in horizontal lines, though rising higher on the shores where the tide rises highest, so have the living waters left their living drift on our mountain-summits, in a line gently rising from the arctic lowlands to a great height under the equator. The various beings thus left stranded may be compared with savage races of man, driven up and surviving in the mountain-fastnesses of almost every land, which serve as a record, full of interest to us, of the former inhabitants of the surrounding lowlands.

Geographical Distribution – continued

As lakes and river-systems are separated from each other by barriers of land, it might have been thought that fresh-water productions would not have ranged widely within the same country, and as the sea is apparently a still more impassable barrier, that they never would have extended to distant countries. But the case is exactly the reverse. Not only have many fresh-water species, belonging to quite different classes, an enormous range, but allied species prevail in a remarkable manner throughout the world. I well remember, when first collecting in the fresh waters of Brazil, feeling much surprise at the similarity of the fresh-water insects, shells, &c., and at the dissimilarity of the surrounding terrestrial beings, compared with those of Britain.

But this power in fresh-water productions of ranging widely, though so unexpected, can, I think, in most cases be explained by their having become fitted, in a manner highly useful to them, for short and frequent migrations from pond to pond, or from stream to stream; and liability to wide dispersal would follow from this capacity as an almost necessary consequence. We can here consider only a few cases. In regard to fish, I believe that the same species never occur in the fresh waters of distant continents. But on the same continent the species often range widely and almost capriciously; for two river-systems will have some fish in common and some different. A few facts seem to favour the possibility of their occasional transport by accidental means; like that of the live fish not rarely dropped by whirlwinds in India, and the vitality of their ova when removed from the water. But I am inclined to attribute the dispersal of fresh-water fish mainly to slight changes within the recent period in the level of the land, having caused rivers to flow into each other. Instances, also, could be given of this having occurred during floods, without any change of level. We have evidence in the loess of the Rhine of considerable changes of level in the land within a very recent geological period, and when the surface was peopled by existing land and fresh-water shells. The wide difference of the fish on opposite sides of continuous mountain-ranges, which from an early period must have parted river-systems and completely prevented their inosculation, seems to lead to this same conclusion. With respect to allied fresh-water fish occurring at very distant points of the world, no doubt there are many cases which cannot at present be explained: but some fresh-water fish belong to very ancient forms, and in such cases there will have been ample time for great geographical changes, and consequently time and means for much migration. In the second place, salt-water fish can with care be slowly accustomed to live in fresh water; and, according to Valenciennes, there is hardly a single group of fishes confined exclusively to fresh water, so that we may imagine that a marine member of a fresh-water group might travel far along the shores of the sea, and subsequently become modified and adapted to the fresh waters of a distant land.

Some species of fresh-water shells have a very wide range, and allied species, which, on my theory, are descended from a common parent and must have proceeded from a single source, prevail throughout the world. Their distribution at first perplexed me much, as their ova are not likely to be transported by birds, and they are immediately killed by sea-water, as are the adults. I could not even understand how some naturalised species have rapidly spread throughout the same country. But two facts, which I have observed – and no doubt many others remain to be observed – throw some light on this subject. When a duck suddenly emerges from a pond covered with duck-weed, I have twice seen these little plants adhering to its back; and it has happened to me, in removing a little duck-weed from one aquarium to another, that I have quite unintentionally stocked the one with fresh-water shells from the other. But another agency is perhaps more effectual: I suspended a duck's feet, which might represent those of a bird sleeping in a natural pond, in an aquarium, where many ova of fresh-water shells were hatching; and I found that numbers of the extremely minute and just hatched shells crawled on the feet, and clung to them so firmly that when taken out of the water they could not be jarred off, though at a somewhat more advanced age they would voluntarily drop off. These just hatched molluscs, though aquatic in their nature, survived on the duck's feet, in damp air, from twelve to twenty hours; and in this length of time a duck or heron might fly at least six or seven hundred miles, and would be sure to alight on a pool or rivulet, if blown across sea to an oceanic island or to any other distant point. Sir Charles Lyell also informs me that a Dyticus has been caught with an Ancylus (a fresh-water shell like a limpet) firmly adhering to it; and a water-beetle of the same family, a Colymbetes, once flew on board the *Beagle*, when forty-five miles distant from the nearest land: how much farther it might have flown with a favouring gale no one can tell.

With respect to plants, it has long been known what enormous ranges many fresh-water and even marsh-species have, both over continents and to the most remote oceanic islands. This is strikingly shown, as remarked by Alph. de Candolle, in large groups of terrestrial plants, which have only a very few aquatic members; for these latter seem immediately to acquire, as if in consequence, a very wide range. I think favourable means of dispersal explain this fact. I have before mentioned that earth occasionally, though rarely, adheres in some quantity to the feet and beaks of birds. Wading birds, which frequent the muddy edges of ponds, if suddenly flushed, would be the most likely to have muddy feet. Birds of this order I can show are the greatest wanderers, and are occasionally found on the most remote and barren islands in the open ocean; they would not be likely to alight on the surface of the sea, so that the dirt would not be washed off their feet; when making land, they would be sure to fly to their natural fresh-water haunts. I do not believe that botanists are aware how charged the mud of ponds is with seeds: I have tried several little experiments, but will here give only the most striking case: I took in February three table-spoonfuls of mud from three different points, beneath water, on the edge of a little pond; this mud when dry weighed only 6¾ ounces; I kept it covered up in my study for six months, pulling up and counting each plant as it grew; the plants were of many kinds, and were altogether 537 in number; and yet the viscid mud was all contained in a breakfast cup! Considering these facts, I think it would be an inexplicable circumstance if water-birds did not transport the seeds of fresh-water plants to vast distances, and if consequently the range of these plants was not very great. The same agency may have come into play with the eggs of some of the smaller fresh-water animals.

Other and unknown agencies probably have also played a part. I have stated that fresh-water fish eat some kinds of seeds, though they reject many other kinds after having swallowed them; even small fish swallow seeds of moderate size, as of the yellow water-lily and Potamogeton. Herons and other birds, century after century, have gone on daily devouring fish; they then take flight and go to other waters, or are blown across the sea; and we have seen that seeds retain their power of germination, when rejected in pellets or in excrement, many hours afterwards. When I saw the great size of the seeds of that fine water-lily, the Nelumbium, and remembered Alph. de Candolle's remarks on this plant, I thought that its distribution must remain quite inexplicable; but Audubon states that he found the seeds of the great southern water-lily (probably, according to Dr Hooker, the Nelumbium luteum) in a heron's stomach; although I do not know the fact, yet analogy makes me believe that a heron flying to another pond and getting a hearty meal of fish, would probably reject from its stomach a pellet containing the seeds of the Nelumbium undigested; or the seeds might be dropped by the bird whilst feeding its young, in the same way as fish are known sometimes to be dropped.

In considering these several means of distribution, it should be remembered that when a pond or stream is first formed, for instance, on a rising islet, it will be unoccupied; and a single seed or egg will have a good chance of succeeding. Although there will always be a struggle for life between the individuals of the species, however few, already occupying any pond, yet as the number of kinds is small, compared with those on the land, the competition will probably be less severe between aquatic than between terrestrial species; consequently an intruder from the waters of a foreign country, would have a better chance of seizing on a place, than in the case of terrestrial colonists. We should, also, remember that some, perhaps many, fresh-water productions are low in the scale of nature, and that we have reason to believe that such low beings change or become modified less quickly than the high; and this will give longer time than the average for the migration of the same aquatic species. We should not forget the probability of many species having formerly ranged as continuously as fresh-water productions ever can range, over immense areas, and having subsequently become extinct in intermediate regions. But the wide distribution of fresh-water plants and of the lower animals, whether retaining the same identical form or in some degree modified, I believe mainly depends on the wide dispersal of their seeds and eggs by animals, more especially by fresh-water birds, which have large powers of flight, and naturally travel from one to another and often distant piece of water. Nature, like a careful gardener, thus takes her seeds from a bed of a particular nature, and drops them in another equally well fitted for them.

On the Inhabitants of Oceanic Islands – We now come to the last of the three classes of facts, which I have selected as presenting the greatest amount of difficulty, on the view that all the individuals both of the same and of allied species have descended from a single parent; and therefore have all proceeded from a common birthplace, notwithstanding that in the course of time they have come to inhabit distant points of the globe. I have already stated that I cannot honestly admit Forbes's view on continental extensions, which, if legitimately followed out, would lead to the belief that within the recent period all existing islands have been nearly or quite joined to some continent. This view would remove many difficulties, but it would not, I think, explain all the facts in regard to insular productions. In the following remarks I shall not confine myself to the mere question of dispersal; but shall consider some other facts, which bear on the truth of the two theories of independent creation and of descent with modification.

The species of all kinds which inhabit oceanic islands are few in number compared with those on equal continental areas: Alph. de Candolle admits this for plants, and Wollaston for insects. If we look to the large size and varied stations of New Zealand, extending over 780 miles of latitude, and compare its flowering plants, only 750 in number, with those on an equal area at the Cape of Good Hope or in Australia, we must, I think, admit that something quite independently of any difference in physical conditions has caused so great a difference in number. Even the uniform county of Cambridge has 847 plants, and the little island of Anglesea 764, but a few ferns and a few introduced plants are included in these numbers, and the comparison in some other respects is not quite fair. We have evidence that the barren island of Ascension aboriginally possessed under half-a-dozen flowering plants; yet many have become naturalised on it, as they have on New Zealand and on every other oceanic island which can be named. In St Helena there is reason to believe that the naturalised plants and animals have nearly or quite exterminated many native productions. He who admits the doctrine of the creation of each separate species, will have to admit, that a sufficient number of the best adapted plants and animals have not been created on oceanic islands; for man has unintentionally stocked them from various sources far more fully and perfectly than has nature.

Although in oceanic islands the number of kinds of inhabitants is scanty, the proportion of endemic species (*i. e.* those found nowhere else in the world) is often extremely large. If we compare, for instance, the number of the endemic land-shells in Madeira, or of the endemic birds in the Galapagos Archipelago, with the number found on any continent, and then compare the area of the islands with that of the continent, we shall see that this is true. This fact might have been expected on my theory, for, as already explained, species occasionally arriving after long intervals in a new and isolated district, and having to compete with new associates, will be eminently liable to modification, and will often produce groups of modified descendants. But it by no means follows, that, because in an island nearly all the species of one class are peculiar, those of another class, or of another section of the same class, are peculiar; and this difference seems to depend on the species which do not become modified having immigrated with facility and in a body, so that their mutual relations have not been much disturbed. Thus in the Galapagos Islands nearly every land-bird, but only two out of the eleven marine birds, are peculiar; and it is obvious that marine birds could arrive at these islands more easily than land-birds. Bermuda, on the other hand, which lies at about the same distance from North America as the Galapagos Islands do from South America, and which has a very peculiar soil, does not possess one endemic land-bird; and we know from Mr J. M. Jones's admirable account of Bermuda, that very many North American birds, during their great annual migrations, visit either periodically or occasionally this island. Madeira does not possess one peculiar bird, and many European and African birds are almost every year blown there, as I am informed by Mr E. V. Harcourt. So that these two islands of Bermuda and Madeira have been stocked by birds, which for long ages have struggled together in their former homes, and have become mutually adapted to each other; and when settled in their new homes, each kind will have been kept by the others to their proper places and habits, and will consequently have been little liable to modification. Madeira, again, is inhabited by a wonderful number of peculiar land-shells, whereas not one species of sea-shell is confined to its shores: now, though we do not know how sea-shells are dispersed, yet we can see that their eggs or larvae, perhaps attached to seaweed or floating timber, or to the feet of wading-birds, might be transported far more easily than land-shells, across three or four hundred miles of open sea. The different orders of insects in Madeira apparently present analogous facts.

Oceanic islands are sometimes deficient in certain classes, and their places are apparently occupied by the other inhabitants; in the Galapagos Islands reptiles, and in New Zealand gigantic wingless birds, take the place of mammals. In the plants of the Galapagos Islands, Dr Hooker has shown that the proportional numbers of the different orders are very different from what they are elsewhere. Such cases are generally accounted for by the physical conditions of the islands; but this explanation seems to me not a little doubtful. Facility of immigration, I believe, has been at least as important as the nature of the conditions.

Many remarkable little facts could be given with respect to the inhabitants of remote islands. For instance, in certain islands not tenanted by mammals, some of the endemic plants have beautifully hooked seeds; yet few relations are more striking than the adaptation of hooked seeds for transportal by the wool and fur of quadrupeds. This case presents no difficulty on my view, for a hooked seed might be transported to an island by some other means; and the plant then becoming slightly modified, but still retaining its hooked seeds, would form an endemic species, having as useless an appendage as any rudimentary organ – for instance, as the shrivelled wings under the soldered elytra of many insular beetles. Again, islands often possess trees or bushes belonging to orders which elsewhere include only herbaceous species; now trees, as Alph. de Candolle has shown, generally have, whatever the cause may be, confined ranges. Hence trees would be little likely to reach distant oceanic islands; and an herbaceous plant, though it would have no chance of successfully competing in stature with a fully developed tree, when established on an island and having to compete with herbaceous plants alone, might readily gain an advantage by growing taller and taller and overtopping the other plants. If so, natural selection would often tend to add to the stature of herbaceous plants when growing on an island, to whatever order they belonged, and thus convert them first into bushes and ultimately into trees.

With respect to the absence of whole orders on oceanic islands, Bory St Vincent long ago remarked that Batrachians (frogs, toads, newts) have never been found on any of the many islands with which the great oceans are studded. I have taken pains to verify this assertion, and I have found it strictly true. I have, however, been assured that a frog exists on the mountains of the great island of New Zealand; but I suspect that this exception (if the information be correct) may be explained through glacial agency. This general absence of frogs, toads, and newts on so many oceanic islands cannot be accounted for by their physical conditions; indeed it seems that islands are peculiarly well fitted for these animals; for frogs have been introduced into Madeira, the Azores, and Mauritius, and have multiplied so as to become a nuisance. But as these animals and their spawn are known to be immediately killed by sea-water, on my view we can see that there would be great difficulty in their transportal across the sea, and therefore why they do not exist on any oceanic island. But why, on the theory of creation, they should not have been created there, it would be very difficult to explain.

Mammals offer another and similar case. I have carefully searched the oldest voyages, but have not finished my search; as yet I have not found a single instance, free from doubt, of a terrestrial mammal (excluding domesticated animals kept by the natives) inhabiting an island situated above 300 miles from a continent or great continental island; and many islands situated at a much less distance are equally barren. The Falkland Islands, which are inhabited by a wolf-like fox, come nearest to an exception; but this group cannot be considered as oceanic, as it lies on a bank connected with the mainland; moreover, icebergs formerly brought boulders to its western shores, and they may have formerly transported foxes, as so frequently now happens in the arctic regions. Yet it cannot be said that small islands will not support small mammals, for they occur in many parts of the world on very small islands, if close to a continent; and hardly an island can be named on which our smaller quadrupeds have not become naturalised and greatly multiplied. It cannot be said, on the ordinary view of creation, that there has not been time for the creation of mammals; many volcanic islands are sufficiently ancient, as shown by the stupendous degradation which they have suffered and by their tertiary strata: there has also been time for the production of endemic species belonging to other classes; and on continents it is thought that mammals appear and disappear at a quicker rate than other and lower animals. Though terrestrial mammals do not occur on oceanic islands, aërial mammals do occur on almost every island. New Zealand possesses two bats found nowhere else in the world: Norfolk Island, the Viti Archipelago, the Bonin Islands, the Caroline and Marianne Archipelagos, and Mauritius, all possess their peculiar bats. Why, it may be asked, has the supposed creative force produced bats and no other mammals on remote islands? On my view this question can easily be answered; for no terrestrial mammals can be transported across a wide space of sea, but bats can fly across. Bats have been seen wandering by day far over the Atlantic Ocean; and two North American species either regularly or occasionally visit Bermuda, at the distance of 600 miles from the mainland. I hear from Mr Tomes, who has specially studied this family, that many of the same species have enormous ranges, and are found on continents and on far distant islands. Hence we have only to suppose that such wandering species have been modified through natural selection in their new homes in relation to their new position, and we can understand the presence of endemic bats on islands, with the absence of all terrestrial mammals.

Besides the absence of terrestrial mammals in relation to the remoteness of islands from continents, there is also a relation, to a certain extent independent of distance, between the depth of the sea separating an island from the neighbouring mainland, and the presence in both of the same mammiferous species or of allied species in a more or less modified condition. Mr Windsor Earl has made some striking observations on this head in regard to the great Malay Archipelago, which is traversed near Celebes by a space of deep ocean; and this space separates two widely distinct mammalian faunas. On either side the islands are situated on moderately deep submarine banks, and they are inhabited by closely allied or identical quadrupeds. No doubt some few anomalies occur in this great archipelago, and there is much difficulty in forming a judgment in some cases owing to the probable naturalisation of certain mammals through man's agency; but we shall soon have much light thrown on the natural history of this archipelago by the admirable zeal and researches of Mr Wallace. I have not as yet had time to follow up this subject in all other quarters of the world; but as far as I have gone, the relation generally holds good. We see Britain separated by a shallow channel from Europe, and the mammals are the same on both sides; we meet with analogous facts on many islands separated by similar channels from Australia. The West Indian Islands stand on a deeply submerged bank, nearly 1000 fathoms in depth, and here we find American forms, but the species and even the genera are distinct. As the amount of modification in all cases depends to a certain degree on the lapse of time, and as during changes of level it is obvious that islands separated by shallow channels are more likely to have been continuously united within a recent period to the mainland than islands separated by deeper channels, we can understand the frequent relation between the depth of the sea and the degree of affinity of the mammalian inhabitants of islands with those of a neighbouring continent – an inexplicable relation on the view of independent acts of creation.

All the foregoing remarks on the inhabitants of ocean-ic islands – namely, the scarcity of kinds – the richness in endemic forms in particular classes or sections of classes – the absence of whole groups, as of batrachians, and of terrestrial mammals notwithstanding the pres-ence of aërial bats – the singular proportions of certain orders of plants – herbaceous forms having been developed into trees, &c. – seem to me to accord better with the view of occasional means of transport having been largely efficient in the long course of time, than with the view of all our oceanic islands having been for-merly connected by continuous land with the nearest continent; for on this latter view the migration would probably have been more complete; and if modification be admitted, all the forms of life would have been more equally modified, in accordance with the paramount importance of the relation of organism to organism.

I do not deny that there are many and grave difficulties in understanding how several of the inhabitants of the more remote islands, whether still retaining the same specific form or modified since their arrival, could have reached their present homes. But the probability of many islands having existed as halting-places, of which not a wreck now remains, must not be overlooked. I will here give a single instance of one of the cases of difficulty. Almost all oceanic islands, even the most isolated and smallest, are inhabited by land-shells, generally by endemic species, but sometimes by species found elsewhere. Dr Aug. A. Gould has given several interesting cases in regard to the land-shells of the islands of the Pacific. Now it is notor-ious that land-shells are very easily killed by salt; their eggs, at least such as I have tried, sink in sea-water and are killed by it. Yet there must be, on my view, some unknown, but highly efficient means for their transportal. Would the just-hatched young occasionally crawl on and adhere to the feet of birds roosting on the ground, and thus get transported? It occurred to me that land-shells, when hybernating and having a membranous diaphragm over the mouth of the shell, might be floated in chinks of drifted timber across moderately wide arms of the sea. And I found that several species did in this state withstand uninjured an immersion in sea-water during seven days: one of these shells was the Helix pomatia, and after it had again hybernated I put it in sea-water for twenty days, and it perfectly recovered. As this species has a thick calcareous operculum, I removed it, and when it had formed a new membranous one, I immersed it for fourteen days in sea-water, and it recovered and crawled away: but more experiments are wanted on this head.

The most striking and important fact for us in regard to the inhabitants of islands, is their affinity to those of the nearest mainland, without being actually the same species. Numerous instances could be given of this fact. I will give only one, that of the Galapagos Archipelago, situated under the equator, between 500 and 600 miles from the shores of South America. Here almost every product of the land and water bears the unmistakeable stamp of the American continent. There are twenty-six land-birds, and twenty-five of these are ranked by Mr Gould as distinct species, supposed to have been created here; yet the close affinity of most of these birds to American species in every character, in their habits, gestures, and tones of voice, was manifest. So it is with the other animals, and with nearly all the plants, as shown by Dr Hooker in his admirable memoir on the Flora of this archipelago. The naturalist, looking at the inhabitants of these volcanic islands in the Pacific, distant several hundred miles from the continent, yet feels that he is standing on American land. Why should this be so? why should the species which are supposed to have been created in the Galapagos Archipelago, and nowhere else, bear so plain a stamp of affinity to those created in America? There is nothing in the conditions of life, in the geological nature of the islands, in their height or climate, or in the proportions in which the several classes are associated together, which resembles closely the conditions of the South American coast: in fact there is a considerable dissimilarity in all these respects. On the other hand, there is a considerable degree of resemblance in the volcanic nature of the soil, in climate, height, and size of the islands, between the Galapagos and Cape de Verde Archipelagos: but what an entire and absolute difference in their inhabitants! The inhabitants of the Cape de Verde Islands are related to those of Africa, like those of the Galapagos to America. I believe this grand fact can receive no sort of explanation on the ordinary view of independent creation; whereas on the view here maintained, it is obvious that the Galapagos Islands would be likely to receive colonists, whether by occasional means of transport or by formerly continuous land, from America; and the Cape de Verde Islands from Africa; and that such colonists would be liable to modification; – the principle of inheritance still betraying their original birthplace.

Many analogous facts could be given: indeed it is an almost universal rule that the endemic productions of islands are related to those of the nearest continent, or of other near islands. The exceptions are few, and most of them can be explained. Thus the plants of Kerguelen Land, though standing nearer to Africa than to America, are related, and that very closely, as we know from Dr Hooker's account, to those of America: but on the view that this island has been mainly stocked by seeds brought with earth and stones on icebergs, drifted by the prevailing currents, this anomaly disappears. New Zealand in its endemic plants is much more closely related to Australia, the nearest mainland, than to any other region: and this is what might have been expected; but it is also plainly related to South America, which, although the next nearest continent, is so enormously remote, that the fact becomes an anomaly. But this difficulty almost disappears on the view that both New Zealand, South America, and other southern lands were long ago partially stocked from a nearly intermediate though distant point, namely from the antarctic islands, when they were clothed with vegetation, before the commencement of the Glacial period. The affinity, which, though feeble, I am assured by Dr Hooker is real, between the flora of the south-western corner of Australia and of the Cape of Good Hope, is a far more remarkable case, and is at present inexplicable: but this affinity is confined to the plants, and will, I do not doubt, be some day explained.

The law which causes the inhabitants of an archipelago, though specifically distinct, to be closely allied to those of the nearest continent, we sometimes see displayed on a small scale, yet in a most interesting manner, within the limits of the same archipelago. Thus the several islands of the Galapagos Archipelago are tenanted, as I have elsewhere shown, in a quite marvellous manner, by very closely related species; so that the inhabitants of each separate island, though mostly distinct, are related in an incomparably closer degree to each other than to the inhabitants of any other part of the world. And this is just what might have been expected on my view, for the islands are situated so near each other that they would almost certainly receive immigrants from the same original source, or from each other. But this dissimilarity between the endemic inhabitants of the islands may be used as an argument against my views; for it may be asked, how has it happened in the several islands situated within sight of each other, having the same geological nature, the same height, climate, &c., that many of the immigrants should have been differently modified, though only in a small degree. This long appeared to me a great difficulty: but it arises in chief part from the deeply-seated error of considering the physical conditions of a country as the most important for its inhabitants; whereas it cannot, I think, be disputed that the nature of the other inhabitants, with which each has to compete, is at least as important, and generally a far more important element of success. Now if we look to those inhabitants of the Galapagos Archipelago which are found in other parts of the world (laying on one side for the moment the endemic species, which cannot be here fairly included, as we are considering how they have come to be modified since their arrival), we find a considerable amount of difference in the several islands. This difference might indeed have been expected on the view of the islands having been stocked by occasional means of transport – a seed, for instance, of one plant having been brought to one island, and that of another plant to another island. Hence when in former times an immigrant settled on any one or more of the islands, or when it subsequently spread from one island to another, it would undoubtedly be exposed to different conditions of life in the different islands, for it would have to compete with different sets of organisms: a plant, for instance, would find the best-fitted ground more perfectly occupied by distinct plants in one island than in another, and it would be exposed to the attacks of somewhat different enemies. If then it varied, natural selection would probably favour different varieties in the different islands. Some species, however, might spread and yet retain the same character throughout the group, just as we see on continents some species spreading widely and remaining the same.

The really surprising fact in this case of the Galapagos Archipelago, and in a lesser degree in some analogous instances, is that the new species formed in the separate islands have not quickly spread to the other islands. But the islands, though in sight of each other, are separated by deep arms of the sea, in most cases wider than the British Channel, and there is no reason to suppose that they have at any former period been continuously united. The currents of the sea are rapid and sweep across the archipelago, and gales of wind are extraordinarily rare; so that the islands are far more effectually separated from each other than they appear to be on a map. Nevertheless a good many species, both those found in other parts of the world and those confined to the archipelago, are common to the several islands, and we may infer from certain facts that these have probably spread from some one island to the others. But we often take, I think, an erroneous view of the probability of closely allied species invading each other's territory, when put into free intercommunication. Undoubtedly if one species has any advantage whatever over another, it will in a very brief time wholly or in part supplant it; but if both are equally well fitted for their own places in nature, both probably will hold their own places and keep separate for almost any length of time. Being familiar with the fact that many species, naturalised through man's agency, have spread with astonishing rapidity over new countries, we are apt to infer that most species would thus spread; but we should remember that the forms which become naturalised in new countries are not generally closely allied to the aboriginal inhabitants, but are very distinct species, belonging in a large proportion of cases, as shown by Alph. de Candolle, to distinct genera. In the Galapagos Archipelago, many even of the birds, though so well adapted for flying from island to island, are distinct on each; thus there are three closely-allied species of mocking-thrush, each confined to its own island. Now let us suppose the mocking-thrush of Chatham Island to be blown to Charles Island, which has its own mocking-thrush: why should it succeed in establishing itself there? We may safely infer that Charles Island is well stocked with its own species, for annually more eggs are laid there than can possibly be reared; and we may infer that the mocking-thrush peculiar to Charles Island is at least as well fitted for its home as is the species peculiar to Chatham Island. Sir C. Lyell and Mr Wollaston have communicated to me a remarkable fact bearing on this subject; namely, that Madeira and the adjoining islet of Porto Santo possess many distinct but representative land-shells, some of which live in crevices of stone; and although large quantities of stone are annually transported from Porto Santo to Madeira, yet this latter island has not become colonised by the Porto Santo species: nevertheless both islands have been colonised by some European land-shells, which no doubt had some advantage over the indigenous species. From these considerations I think we need not greatly marvel at the endemic and representative species, which inhabit the several islands of the Galapagos Archipelago, not having universally spread from island to island. In many other instances, as in the several districts of the same continent, pre-occupation has probably played an important part in checking the commingling of species under the same conditions of life. Thus, the south-east and south-west corners of Australia have nearly the same physical conditions, and are united by continuous land, yet they are inhabited by a vast number of distinct mammals, birds, and plants.

The principle which determines the general character of the fauna and flora of oceanic islands, namely, that the inhabitants, when not identically the same, yet are plainly related to the inhabitants of that region whence colonists could most readily have been derived – the colonists having been subsequently modified and better fitted to their new homes – is of the widest application throughout nature. We see this on every mountain, in every lake and marsh. For Alpine species, excepting in so far as the same forms, chiefly of plants, have spread widely throughout the world during the recent Glacial epoch, are related to those of the surrounding lowlands; – thus we have in South America, Alpine humming-birds, Alpine rodents, Alpine plants, &c., all of strictly American forms, and it is obvious that a mountain, as it became slowly upheaved, would naturally be colonised from the surrounding lowlands. So it is with the inhabitants of lakes and marshes, excepting in so far as great facility of transport has given the same general forms to the whole world. We see this same principle in the blind animals inhabiting the caves of America and of Europe. Other analogous facts could be given. And it will, I believe, be universally found to be true, that wherever in two regions, let them be ever so distant, many closely allied or representative species occur, there will likewise be found some identical species, showing, in accordance with the foregoing view, that at some former period there has been intercommunication or migration between the two regions. And wherever many closely-allied species occur, there will be found many forms which some naturalists rank as distinct species, and some as varieties; these doubtful forms showing us the steps in the process of modification.

This relation between the power and extent of migration of a species, either at the present time or at some former period under different physical conditions, and the existence at remote points of the world of other species allied to it, is shown in another and more general way. Mr Gould remarked to me long ago, that in those genera of birds which range over the world, many of the species have very wide ranges. I can hardly doubt that this rule is generally true, though it would be difficult to prove it. Amongst mammals, we see it strikingly displayed in Bats, and in a lesser degree in the Felidae and Canidae. We see it, if we compare the distribution of butterflies and beetles. So it is with most fresh-water productions, in which so many genera range over the world, and many individual species have enormous ranges. It is not meant that in world-ranging genera all the species have a wide range, or even that they have on an *average* a wide range; but only that some of the species range very widely; for the facility with which widely-ranging species vary and give rise to new forms will largely determine their average range. For instance, two varieties of the same species inhabit America and Europe, and the species thus has an immense range; but, if the variation had been a little greater, the two varieties would have been ranked as distinct species, and the common range would have been greatly reduced. Still less is it meant, that a species which apparently has the capacity of crossing barriers and ranging widely, as in the case of certain powerfully-winged birds, will necessarily range widely; for we should never forget that to range widely implies not only the power of crossing barriers, but the more important power of being victorious in distant lands in the struggle for life with foreign associates. But on the view of all the species of a genus having descended from a single parent, though now distributed to the most remote points of the world, we ought to find, and I believe as a general rule we do find, that some at least of the species range very widely;

for it is necessary that the unmodified parent should range widely, undergoing modification during its diffusion, and should place itself under diverse conditions favourable for the conversion of its offspring, firstly into new varieties and ultimately into new species.

In considering the wide distribution of certain genera, we should bear in mind that some are extremely ancient, and must have branched off from a common parent at a remote epoch; so that in such cases there will have been ample time for great climatal and geographical changes and for accidents of transport; and consequently for the migration of some of the species into all quarters of the world, where they may have become slightly modified in relation to their new conditions. There is, also, some reason to believe from geological evidence that organisms low in the scale within each great class, generally change at a slower rate than the higher forms; and consequently the lower forms will have had a better chance of ranging widely and of still retaining the same specific character. This fact, together with the seeds and eggs of many low forms being very minute and better fitted for distant transportation, probably accounts for a law which has long been observed, and which has lately been admirably discussed by Alph. de Candolle in regard to plants, namely, that the lower any group of organisms is, the more widely it is apt to range.

The relations just discussed – namely, low and slowly-changing organisms ranging more widely than the high – some of the species of widely-ranging genera themselves ranging widely – such facts, as alpine, lacustrine, and marsh productions being related (with the exceptions

before specified) to those on the surrounding low lands
and dry lands, though these stations are so different – the
very close relation of the distinct species which inhabit
the islets of the same archipelago – and especially the
striking relation of the inhabitants of each whole archipelago or island to those of the nearest mainland – are, I
think, utterly inexplicable on the ordinary view of the
independent creation of each species, but are explicable
on the view of colonisation from the nearest and readiest
source, together with the subsequent modification and
better adaptation of the colonists to their new homes.

Summary of last and present Chapters – In these chapters I
have endeavoured to show, that if we make due allowance for our ignorance of the full effects of all the changes
of climate and of the level of the land, which have certainly occurred within the recent period, and of other
similar changes which may have occurred within the
same period; if we remember how profoundly ignorant
we are with respect to the many and curious means
of occasional transport – a subject which has hardly ever
been properly experimentised on; if we bear in mind
how often a species may have ranged continuously over
a wide area, and then have become extinct in the intermediate tracts, I think the difficulties in believing that all
the individuals of the same species, wherever located,
have descended from the same parents, are not insuperable. And we are led to this conclusion, which has been
arrived at by many naturalists under the designation of
single centres of creation, by some general considerations, more especially from the importance of barriers

and from the analogical distribution of sub-genera, genera, and families.

With respect to the distinct species of the same genus, which on my theory must have spread from one parent-source; if we make the same allowances as before for our ignorance, and remember that some forms of life change most slowly, enormous periods of time being thus granted for their migration, I do not think that the difficulties are insuperable; though they often are in this case, and in that of the individuals of the same species, extremely grave.

As exemplifying the effects of climatal changes on distribution, I have attempted to show how important has been the influence of the modern Glacial period, which I am fully convinced simultaneously affected the whole world, or at least great meridional belts. As showing how diversified are the means of occasional transport, I have discussed at some little length the means of dispersal of fresh-water productions.

If the difficulties be not insuperable in admitting that in the long course of time the individuals of the same species, and likewise of allied species, have proceeded from some one source; then I think all the grand leading facts of geographical distribution are explicable on the theory of migration (generally of the more dominant forms of life), together with subsequent modification and the multiplication of new forms. We can thus understand the high importance of barriers, whether of land or water, which separate our several zoological and botanical provinces. We can thus understand the localisation of sub-genera, genera, and families; and how it is that under different latitudes, for instance in South America, the inhabitants of the plains and mountains, of the forests, marshes, and deserts, are in so mysterious a manner linked together by affinity, and are likewise linked to the extinct beings which formerly inhabited the same continent. Bearing in mind that the mutual relations of organism to organism are of the highest importance, we can see why two areas having nearly the same physical conditions should often be inhabited by very different forms of life; for according to the length of time which has elapsed since new inhabitants entered one region; according to the nature of the communication which allowed certain forms and not others to enter, either in greater or lesser numbers; according or not, as those which entered happened to come in more or less direct competition with each other and with the aborigines; and according as the immigrants were capable of varying more or less rapidly, there would ensue in different regions, independently of their physical conditions, infinitely diversified conditions of life – there would be an almost endless amount of organic action and reaction – and we should find, as we do find, some groups of beings greatly, and some only slightly modified – some developed in great force, some existing in scanty numbers – in the different great geographical provinces of the world.

On these same principles, we can understand, as I have endeavoured to show, why oceanic islands should have few inhabitants, but of these a great number should be endemic or peculiar; and why, in relation to the means of migration, one group of beings, even within the same class, should have all its species endemic, and another group should have all its species common to other quarters of the world. We can see why whole groups of organisms, as batrachians and terrestrial mammals, should be absent from oceanic islands, whilst the most isolated islands possess their own peculiar species of aërial mammals or bats. We can see why there should be some relation between the presence of mammals, in a more or less modified condition, and the depth of the sea between an island and the mainland. We can clearly see why all the inhabitants of an archipelago, though specifically distinct on the several islets, should be closely related to each other, and likewise be related, but less closely, to those of the nearest continent or other source whence immigrants were probably derived. We can see why in two areas, however distant from each other, there should be a correlation, in the presence of identical species, of varieties, of doubtful species, and of distinct but representative species.

As the late Edward Forbes often insisted, there is a striking parallelism in the laws of life throughout time and space: the laws governing the succession of forms in past times being nearly the same with those governing at the present time the differences in different areas. We see this in many facts. The endurance of each species and group of species is continuous in time; for the exceptions to the rule are so few, that they may fairly be attributed to our not having as yet discovered in an intermediate deposit the forms which are therein absent, but which occur above and below: so in space, it certainly is the general rule that the area inhabited by a single species, or by a group of species, is continuous; and the exceptions, which are not rare, may, as I have attempted to show, be accounted for by migration at some former period under different conditions or by occasional means of transport, and by the species having become extinct in the intermediate tracts. Both in time and space, species and groups of species have their points of maximum development. Groups of species, belonging either to a certain period of time, or to a certain area, are often characterised by trifling characters in common, as of sculpture or colour. In looking to the long succession of ages, as in now looking to distant provinces throughout the world, we find that some organisms differ little, whilst others belonging to a different class, or to a different order, or even only to a different family of the same order, differ greatly. In both time and space the lower members of each class generally change less than the higher; but there are in both cases marked exceptions to the rule. On my theory these several relations throughout time and space are intelligible; for whether we look to the forms of life which have changed during successive ages within the same quarter of the world, or to those which have changed after having migrated into distant quarters, in both cases the forms within each class have been connected by the same bond of ordinary generation; and the more nearly any two forms are related in blood, the nearer they will generally stand to each other in time and space; in both cases the laws of variation have been the same, and modifications have been accumulated by the same power of natural selection.

THE STORY OF PENGUIN CLASSICS

Before 1946 ... 'Classics' are mainly the domain of academics and students; readable editions for everyone else are almost unheard of. This all changes when a little-known classicist, E. V. Rieu, presents Penguin founder Allen Lane with the translation of Homer's *Odyssey* that he has been working on in his spare time.

1946 Penguin Classics debuts with *The Odyssey*, which promptly sells three million copies. Suddenly, classics are no longer for the privileged few.

1950s Rieu, now series editor, turns to professional writers for the best modern, readable translations, including Dorothy L. Sayers's *Inferno* and Robert Graves's unexpurgated *Twelve Caesars*.

1960s The Classics are given the distinctive black covers that have remained a constant throughout the life of the series. Rieu retires in 1964, hailing the Penguin Classics list as 'the greatest educative force of the twentieth century.'

1970s A new generation of translators swells the Penguin Classics ranks, introducing readers of English to classics of world literature from more than twenty languages. The list grows to encompass more history, philosophy, science, religion and politics.

1980s The Penguin American Library launches with titles such as *Uncle Tom's Cabin*, and joins forces with Penguin Classics to provide the most comprehensive library of world literature available from any paperback publisher.

1990s The launch of Penguin Audiobooks brings the classics to a listening audience for the first time, and in 1999 the worldwide launch of the Penguin Classics website extends their reach to the global online community.

The 21st Century Penguin Classics are completely redesigned for the first time in nearly twenty years. This world-famous series now consists of more than 1300 titles, making the widest range of the best books ever written available to millions – and constantly redefining what makes a 'classic'.

The Odyssey continues ...

The best books ever written

PENGUIN CLASSICS

SINCE 1946

Find out more at www.penguinclassics.com